Transforming the Difficult Child Workbook:

An Interactive Guide to The Nurtured Heart Approach

For Parents, Teachers, Practitioners
and All Other Caregivers

Howard Glasser

Joann Bowdidge

Lisa Bravo

Transforming the Difficult Child Workbook:
An Interactive Guide to The Nurtured Heart Approach

Copyright – Second Edition, January 2013 by Howard Glasser, Joann Bowdidge, and Lisa Bravo

All rights reserved. No part of this book may be reproduced or utilized in any form or by any means, electronic, mechanical, photocopying, recording, or by any storage and retrieval system, without the permission from the publisher.

The Nurtured Heart Approach is a trademark of the Children's Success Foundation.

For information contact: Nurtured Heart Publications
        4165 West Ironwood Hill Drive
        Tucson, Arizona 85745

For information about bulk purchasing discounts of this book or other Transforming the Difficult Child books, videos, CDs or DVDs, please contact Fulfillment Services at 800-311-3132.

For orders within the book industry, please contact Brigham Distributing at 435-723-6611.

Cover by Michael Kichler, M.A.
Book design by Michael Kichler, M.A.
Copy editing by Chris Howell
Printed by Vaughan Printing, Nashville, TN.

Library of Congress Card Catalogue Number: Pending

ISBN-13: 978-0-9670507-5-1
ISBN-10: 0-9670507-5-8

First Edition: November 2007 - Printed in the United States
Second Edition: January 2013 - Printed in China

TABLE OF CONTENTS

Preface

It's always been a little surreal for me to receive credit for The Nurtured Heart Approach and for all the impact it has had on so many lives. If anything, I feel I was the lucky one who was merely in the right place at the right time and the right person with the right qualifications.

One such qualification was having been a difficult child; another was having had the experience of **NOT** getting to use my intensity well for so many years; another was having experienced the devastating sense of lost time, lost effort and lost dreams.

It was these very experiences that produced within me a passion to make the successful use of this approach so attainable that it allows parents and teachers to renew their love for their children and deeply experience having a positive impact – right from the start of putting this approach into action.

One thing that has meant the most to me was to create this approach in a way that makes so much sense that it causes those hearing about it to react: "Oh my gosh, that's it!" In my experience, that response coming from anyone who is first learning this approach is a key predictor of a great outcome – the outcome parents and teachers are so hoping to achieve.

My co-authors and I believe that, when we encounter a difficult child, whether in the home, classroom, treatment center or our other programs, we *so desperately* want to be influential in their lives. We hope to prove to you by way of this approach that normal methods of attempting to be influential in a positive way are most often going to have the exact opposite effect; and the harder we try, the worse the situation will get.

We also hope to prove to you that, although we think we are reaching our challenging children in a logical and straightforward manner with direct messages of increasing urgency, they are actually responding counter intuitively and counterproductively to unseen messages that run underneath all the words of wisdom we believe we are delivering in the zillion ways we do. We are only kidding ourselves while all the time thinking we are finally going to get through to them and win our point forevermore.

Maybe the one gift in all of this that I can totally take credit for is that, when I started working with families, I began to encounter a strong sensitivity for how **energy was transmitted** in the process of adult-child interactions.

And in the midst of experiencing this gift, I came to see that many children come to form the impression that they get so much greater quality of relationship from adults when things are going wrong. The problem is that this becomes highly addictive! Before long the child gives up trying to be positive because there is much less energy seemingly available, and he begins to ramp up the negativity because he finds the resultant connection and relationship so very present and compelling.

Unfortunately, this impression can trigger children to conclude something even more convoluted – that they are more loved when things are going wrong. That's because they equate the essence of being loved with the reality of when we are really there for them – when we really show up. And traditional methods have us "showing up" so much more when there are problems. No one would ever do that on purpose. But we do it accidentally all the time. We hope to show you that by following the "old school" recommendations you find in the vast majority of books, articles and other parenting sources, the child will progressively get worse.

BUT NOW FOR THE GOOD NEWS! We also hope to show you how utterly easy it is to not only improve your situation with the intense and difficult child, but to actually TRANSFORM that same intensity to the point where it is the source of the child's GREATNESS.

From this point of view, improvement is not really what people want, because with improvement alone, you are still experiencing underlying problems and issues. Even if the problems substantially diminish with the improvement, the adults and child continue to dwell in the shadows of how the child knows himself and others – which is still a problem-oriented relationship.

If the improvement is accomplished through medications, the parent is still none the wiser on how to best help the child, nor is the child any the wiser on how to best help herself. Everyone can easily come to believe in the medications rather than the child, and the unfortunate message to the child is that "something is wrong with you because of your intensity…neither you nor we can handle it." The meta-message is "we need to make it go away." And therein begins the divorce between the child and his life force…his intensity.

We can no longer afford to lose these children to such messages. We can no longer afford to incur the side effects of so much reliance on medications. We can no longer afford to call these symptoms pathology when, in fact, this very same intensity is what propels these children into being better than the average child when a powerful enough approach is applied.

And we believe that we can no longer afford to think in terms of mere improvement when there is now an approach available that can lead these very same children to see how great they are. Once they are led to see this, and they drink from that well, they begin to lead the life of greatness that is their birthright – a life that is so much more than improvements.

We believe that what adults really want for these children, deep in their hearts and souls, is to see them move fully to their new life of living in GREATNESS. This is what we call TRANSFORMATION, and then you truly have the best kid on the block.

And the GREAT NEWS is that there's endless room for best kids on the block.

And that is why we have written this workbook: to provide parents, other caregivers, teachers and practitioners a clear, step-by-step manual to help you acquire the skills needed to begin using The Nurtured Heart Approach – to make it simpler and more understandable than ever. It is our greatest hope that this workbook will give you the courage and assurance to believe you CAN do this. You will be amazingly surprised, delighted and truly grateful when you begin to see how this approach changes the life of your child as well as your own life.

Congratulations in advance for transforming the children to whom you are bringing this approach, and we hope you fully enjoy the process.

Blessings & Miracles!!!

Howard Glasser

A Note about the Word Positivity

Positivity is not an actual word (yet!) But in trying to convey The Nurtured Heart Approach to our readers, we attempted to use other (actual) words and found they either had some interpretive baggage or didn't adequately convey our desired meaning. And since negativity is a word, we felt that it's opposite – positivity – would convey the proper level of vastness we were seeking in our attempts to fully describe the counterpoint of negativity. We therefore took the liberty, in this book, of "inventing" the word positivity to connote the richest sense of being positive. Again, we hope that readers will overlook our incorrectness in this situation and understand our motives.

Howard, Joann and Lisa

INTRODUCTION

Congratulations on your decision to learn a powerful method to bring about positive changes and transformation to the children in your life – The Nurtured Heart Approach™.

Through The Nurtured Heart Approach, we are confident that you will strengthen your relationships and come to celebrate the children in your life. We are honored to guide you through this journey that will undoubtedly change your life and the lives of children in exciting and positive ways.

This workbook is designed to improve your understanding and application of The Nurtured Heart Approach. It is meant to enhance *Transforming the Difficult Child: The Nurtured Heart Approach* by Howard Glasser and Jennifer Easley and the various taped lectures currently available. This workbook is designed to wrap you around the basic notions and techniques of the approach *experientially* so that YOU will become the expert – creating boundless successes to transform the lives and hearts of the children you love.

A Caution

As you progress along the journey of applying Nurtured Heart, please keep in mind that learning a new approach is a process, and some level of daily commitment is necessary in order to gain momentum in the right direction. The Nurtured Heart Approach has proven to be extremely effective in changing behavior and transforming relationships *when it is used with consistency.*

The Nurtured Heart Approach: What is it?

The Nurtured Heart Approach is more than just a parenting or behavior management strategy. It is equally a philosophy for creating healthy relationships with the people in your life. The Nurtured Heart Approach will increase your awareness and understanding of those relationships. Further, you will soon see that Nurtured Heart ultimately is a spiritual approach because it gives you strategies to "capture everyday moments" in an absolutely truthful manner that allows you to reflect back to the child and to celebrate with him his great decisions, judgment and wisdom, thereby allowing him to align with his divine nature and goodness.

This approach is a way of thinking and a set of strategies that are particularly useful for difficult, intense children, but it can also be tremendously valuable for all children. It emphasizes energizing crucial traits of a whole person within the structure of clear and consistent boundaries, with the goal of creating a wonderful new level of "inner wealth" that will inspire the child to make positive choices rather than negative ones. The Nurtured Heart Approach provides <u>just the right amount of balance</u> between being positive with the child and setting limits with the child. *Strong positives* are used in conjunction with *excellent limit setting,* along with a refusal to accidentally reward negativity. (This will all be explained in detail as we go along.)

The Nurtured Heart Approach lays the foundation for a healthy, positive and reciprocal relationship between you and the child. The child will become adept at discerning what is in her best interest and, as a result, will learn to make better choices. Through the methods that we will recommend, the child begins to shift to an inner perception of success and prosperity.

It has been our experience that children who have developed "inner wealth" begin to make choices that reflect a sense of values and character. Nurtured Heart allows the child to become strong on the inside, so that outside influences will be less likely to permeate his judgment. In short, to the extent that you can build the child's inner wealth by nurturing positive behaviors, to that extent he can move forth and learn to use his intensity to flourish in wonderful ways instead of ways that are destructive or alarming. He comes to identify with success.

Where Did The Nurtured Heart Approach Come From?

Howard Glasser was trained in clinical psychology, earning his Master's degree at New York University. His original work as a therapist was mainly with adults. Over time, however, his practice began to shift to families, particularly those with "difficult" children. Glasser discovered from working with families and children that the typical tools of parenting and teaching all worked to some extent with easy children, but they clearly did not work for families with intense, difficult children who thrive on adversity. *In fact, the majority of normal, conventional methods actually made things worse, not better. AND the harder parents tried these normal approaches, the worse it got despite the best of intentions.*

Glasser found that typical parenting methods did not work because they *accidentally rewarded negativity,* thereby inadvertently energizing failure…*almost like accidentally giving the child a hundred dollar bill for making a poor choice.*

His work with these families and children brought back a "total recall" of his own times as a difficult child and the mistakes of those who had tried to help him. This, combined with a growing sense of intuition that he felt was "given to him" in order to help these children and families in distress, led him to develop and hone what ultimately became The Nurtured Heart Approach. When he discovered how phenomenally successful these ideas were in treatment with his client families, he began teaching the approach to other therapists and presenting family workshops.

Glasser discovered that this set of strategies and techniques worked with all levels of severity, diagnostic categories and ages. A few of the many examples:

> For five years he worked with the Juvenile Court in Pima County (Tucson) Arizona. At that time, 50% of first offenders became repeat offenders, committing an average of six subsequent crimes of greater severity prior to turning age 18. During this period, Glasser worked with 1,000 offenders and their families, many of whom did not embrace treatment at first. Using The Nurtured Heart Approach's strategies and techniques, the recidivism rate <u>dropped to less than 16%.</u> Of those who re-offended, there was an average of only one crime, AND that crime was of a less serious nature.

> Tolson Elementary School in Tucson adopted The Nurtured Heart Approach in 1999 and has reported remarkable decreases in student suspensions. The number of students prescribed medication and students diagnosed with behavior disorders has gone down to zero, as has teacher attrition. Special education utilization went from 15% of all students to 1.2%, representing a tremendous savings of human and fiscal resources. Standardized test scores went from failing to excelling in this time period, despite Tolson being a school with a minority population and many at-risk children.

> Glasser also worked with Tucson Head Start, teaching the teachers the strategies and methods of The Nurtured Heart Approach. During the previous seven years, an entire department within the mental health network was devoted to the many children Tucson Head Start referred for services, including diagnosis and medication. Since Head Start began using The Nurtured Heart Approach, the number of mental health referrals has consistently been negligible. Now diagnosis and medication referrals are virtually non-existent, and the savings has allowed the program to serve 1,000 more children and families yearly.

In response to many requests to share this work, Glasser developed seminars to teach others about this approach and the transforming power of its strategies and techniques. Live and online seminars are available; for up-to-date schedules, check the website of the Children's Success Foundation at **www.ChildrensSuccessFoundation.com**. His first book, *Transforming the Difficult Child: The Nurtured Heart Approach*, was published in 1999 and revised in 2008. His most recent book, *Notching Up the Nurtured Heart Approach: the Nurtured Heart Approach for Educators*, was published in 2011. The Nurtured Heart Approach is expanding in scope as parents, schools and other institutions become aware of its dramatic effectiveness.

What are the Basic Premises of The Nurtured Heart Approach?

Here's the central premise of The Nurtured Heart Approach upon which everything is based: If you help a child feel great about who she is, the instances of challenging behavior dissolve and new realms of great choices come to the fore. Now we'll discuss important ideas associated with that premise.

Intensity

First is the idea of intensity. The problem is that challenging children typically use their intensity poorly. In Nurtured Heart thinking, intensity is a good thing because one's intensity, or life force, can be transformed to propel wonderful levels of success. However, today's society treats intensity as a bad thing; for example, the first line of treatment in the medical community is to moderate intensity through medications.

Children, particularly intense children, need to develop the coping skills to deal with the pressures they face on a daily basis. More than ever before, children need to feel "strong on the inside" so that they can discern the positive from the negative and make wise choices, even in the face of negative outside influences. When a child learns to feel great about his intensity, the incidents of challenging behavior dissolve, and a new realm of great choices can come to the foreground. Nurtured Heart shows you how to shift the child to use his intensity in great ways. You will be in the driver's seat when it comes to creating success and positivity in a child's life.

We need our intensity. It drives our life force and gives us the determination to fulfill our life's path. Those who are intense are often more sensitive. But children who are more sensitive, more intense and more needy are often in a compromised position. Just by way of experiencing their intensity, and the truth of how people respond to their actions, they can easily form the misguided impression that they are much more interesting to others and essentially more celebrated (and even perceive they are more loved) by way of poor choices. **They learn that there is so much more relationship and energy flowing when things are going wrong than when things are going right.**

Some children are simply born with more intensity and some develop more through life circumstances. Most of us learn to handle our intensity most of the time, although the best of children still have moments when intensity overwhelms their ability to control it. **But Intensity is not the enemy when we have the inner strength to handle it well.**

Try This!

The next time you are at your local park, mall, or grocery store, observe the interactions between parents and children. Watch how parents respond to a child's poor choice. How did they accidentally energize negativity? Do you see how the child might drink in the experience differently than intended? The parent might be trying to teach an important lesson or set a limit, but the child's reality – her first-hand experience – is that she is relatively invisible when things are okay and of much greater interest to the parent when creating a problem. Why? The child sees much more evidence of relationship and energy flowing.

Transformation

Most methods for dealing with difficult children seek improvement: a shift in the child's behaviors, for example, or better adherence to the rules. In the Nurtured Heart Approach, improvement is not the ultimate goal. These methods are about helping a child to *transform*.

With improvement, underlying issues tend not to go away; we've just found a way to prevent their expression. Problems remain the overall relationship focus. They may be temporarily solved through the use of psychoactive medications, but what happens when the medications are stopped? Medications don't heal. Putting a pharmacologic leash on the child does not improve her ability to deal with her intensity. As soon as the medication is stopped, the same issues come back to the fore.

Medical interventions are often considered when children have difficult behaviors that seem intractable and bound to escalate. And when the difficult child starts to take his Ritalin or other mind-altering medication, he does seem to improve. He calms down; he can focus; he has less trouble getting along with peers and adults. But the parent is no wiser about how to help the child when he isn't medicated. The child is no wiser about how to help himself. Using medications in this context gives the child an unfortunate message: that he can't handle himself and that we can't handle him…that his intensity is not okay and that we need to moderate it or make it disappear because it scares us.

And there begins the divorce between the child and his life force. There begins the child's adversarial relationship with his own intensity. We wind up inadvertently driving a wedge between the child and his belief in himself and his ability to enjoy the propulsion that healthy intensity can provide toward living a fulfilled life. It's life force that helps us energize our purpose and fuels us to envision and to live out our dreams. There's a better way.

We can no longer afford to lose children to such messages. We can't afford the physical or psychological side effects of medication (for more on that, see *101 Reasons to Avoid Ritalin Like the Plague,* Howard's book on this topic) or the reliance we've developed on chemical fixes for relationship problems. These fixes do not produce internal healing or a reservoir of strength inside the child.

Once we see that this same intensity propels these children to greatness when a powerful enough approach is applied, we no longer have to call it pathology. Instead, they move fully into their new life of living in greatness. This is transformation – and with it, the most difficult kid becomes the best kid on the block.

Transformation is internal change – not change from the outside in, but from the inside out. Through Nurtured Heart, the child develops a reservoir of inner wealth that can be drawn upon in times of stress. Improvement pales in comparison with transformation. What people really want for their children isn't to stifle their intensity, but to see it lead them into their intrinsic greatness.

Replacing the Negative Portfolio with a Positive One

Children form their feelings of worth and self-esteem in response to day-to-day feedback from their worlds. They respond when adults notice them most strongly and offer up the most intense and connected relationship in return.

Challenging and intense children get much more attention and interaction in response to poor choices than they do in response to what they do right. As a child tests rules and limits and receives highly charged connection and relationship, she often will feel confronted by criticisms and admonishments that land within her as failures. Statement of limit setting such as "Cut it out!" "Quit that!" or "Stop it!" are absorbed by the child as reflections and messages of failure, even when said lovingly. These encounters, whether subtle or profound, contribute to forming the child's "inner portfolio" – often predominantly comprised of negative thoughts and ideas of herself, based upon these day-by-day experiences of negative feedback.

Once this self-image is established, the child often internally refutes any positive statements others make to her. She believes she's a bad kid; that she's always messing up. "Something is wrong with me. Something is wrong with my brain." This inner defensiveness renders ordinary styles of traditional and conventional praise ineffective.

As such an intense child begins to believe that she gets more out of the adults in her life when choosing poor behaviors, she comes to crave this negativity as a way of obtaining intense connection with those meaningful people in her life. These are the very people who need more encompassing and powerful ways to have a positive impact.

Transformation involves a highly intentional process of replacing the existing negative portfolio with experiences of success and self-worth through an inspired and steady stream of powerful appreciation, recognition and acknowledgment. As her portfolio's basic foundation begins to shift, she begins to see herself as competent and successful. From this place, her behaviors will change – because she's now acting out a new self-image of worthiness and wisdom. What parents and teachers have wanted all along is for this child to act out greatness. When this transpires, everyone emerges a hero – and this is precisely what the Nurtured Heart Approach is about..

When does your child feel most celebrated?

…when making wise choices, or making poor choices?

…when things are going well, or when things are not going well?

The difficult child is more likely to feel celebrated when making poor choices. That is when he may perceive getting more energized connection and relationship from the adults in his life. Consider: under what circumstances does he get a stronger sense of YOU? If it is when things are going wrong, then the child may have a developing or established negative portfolio. You may well have a keen sense of what is inside it. Have you spent time making a list of all the things you wish were different, better or less problematic? Take a moment to think this through and jot down your thoughts.

When Does Your Child Feel Most Celebrated?

<u>Example: When my daughter argues she gets lots of energy and relationship. I keep feeling</u>

<u>that I want to break through her logic and I always accidentally fall into this trap.</u>

A. _____

_____

B. _____

_____

C. _____

_____

The NEWS about Hijacking Our Children to Success

The **UNFORTUNATE NEWS** is that, if unchallenged, children continue to default to the negative portfolio. Behaviors will be consistent with that portfolio and continue to deepen a cycle entrenched in adversity.

The **GOOD NEWS** is that we have the ability to get around the radar and change the portfolio!

The **GREAT NEWS** is that we do not need a child's permission in order to help him shift to a new way of being wonderful. The strategies and techniques in this book will pave the way for your child to experience how great he is and then act that out!

The **FANTASTIC NEWS** is that children with high intensity make the most incredible children because they have so much more life force to channel into positive endeavors.

Do you recall how exponential negativity can be? **SUCCESS CAN BE EXPONENTIAL AS WELL, AND IT'S A LOT MORE FUN TO WITNESS!**

The Transformative Power of Success Experiences

Now Now let's talk about transformation.

Nurtured Heart strategies create success experiences for children that transform them on the inside. They create this impact by teaching children to use their intensity in positive, brilliant and amazing ways. Through this approach, you will increase your awareness of your child's successes, and you'll gain the ability to talk about them with your child in vivid, highly energized language. You will become adept at creating opportunities for energizing success – at seizing everyday moments and reflecting them as proof that the child is living out her greatness.

As you use the Nurtured Heart Approach to create irrefutable experiences of success for your child, she will begin to download these new experiences into an ever-changing, expansive portfolio of success.

We're talking about much more than compliments like "thank you" and "good job." Get ready to move on to a far more expansive way of thinking about and acknowledging what's going right. In the course of learning this approach, you will learn much more powerful forms of recognition and appreciation. When you create goodness in an absolutely truthful moment, transformation begins.

With this approach, we don't just applaud high-level successes like good grades or the winning of awards or sports events. In a determined way, we "confront" the child with successes at every level, from simple desirable behaviors (like staying focused and being calm) to an entirely deeper realm where everyday successes and intrinsic qualities are acknowledged and appreciated in great and creative detail. We're literally hijacking our children into success!

If left unchallenged, the child will continue to default to the negative portfolio. Behaviors will be consistent with that old portfolio. A cycle entrenched in adversity will continue to deepen. The strategies and techniques in this book will pave the way for your child to experience his own greatness. Once he gets a taste of this, he'll act out success without a second thought. When this happens for high-intensity children, it's especially miraculous. They have so much life force to channel into positive endeavors.

Any adult who has gotten sucked into the vortex of negativity knows how things can escalate. From a small problem, a huge maelstrom of problems can arise all too easily. The good news here is that success can grow in exactly the same exponential fashion…and we think you'll agree that success and greatness are much more fun to witness.

Before this can happen, there's an initial step: we change the habitual "default" of focusing on problem behaviors. We resolve to refuse to put our energy there. Why water weeds? What we energize, we encourage. We change what we energize to stop inadvertently giving conflicting messages (that we are more present for a child's poor behaviors, even though we continually admonish the child for engaging in them). Much more on this in chapters to come.

Creating Inner Wealth

Through the creation of success experiences, the Nurtured Heart Approach helps children develop the inner strength they need to be empowered, capable adults who believe in themselves and in others. This is what we call inner wealth.

Inner wealth brings children into alignment with their divine natures and with their highest good. Children with inner wealth are better equipped to tackle life's challenges and to live out their lives in greatness. They are less likely to fall prey to peer pressure or to misbehave, and they treat their bodies and minds with reverence. They learn to live with integrity and purpose and to make choices based on their inner wisdom.

Children who experience inner wealth feel good about themselves; they learn that they can take control of their own intensity and power, and can use it for good; and they develop an unshakable confidence.

Lisa's daughter, who at this writing is in her teens, was raised with this approach and is a shining example of a young person with lots of inner wealth. She is not impressed with trying to fit in with any particular peer group; she relies on her internal wisdom and isn't concerned about pleasing others in a superficial way. If other children are participating in an activity that is not in line with her internal beliefs – for example, teasing another child – she separates herself or even openly advocates for the person being teased. Her choices seem dictated by a powerful and positive internal compass.

An Introduction to the Nurtured Heart Approach: Main Components and Phases

This approach consists of three main components:

1. Refusal to energize or accidentally reward negativity

2. Creating and super-energizing experiences of success

3.   Providing a perfect level of limit-setting and consequences

This book will cover these components in four parts, which we call Phases. The first part will cover Phase I – **Refusing to Energize Negativity and Energizing Success.** Then, we'll move to Phase II, the all-important (but not primary, in this approach) issues of **Limit Setting and Consequences.** Phase III will be all about the **Credit System and Ways to Enhance the Approach's Impact;** and in Phase IV, we'll look at ways to **Extend the Approach to Your Child's School System.**

Phases III and IV are not always called for. When the situation does call for the credit system and for extending Nurtured Heart into a child's school experience, these last two phases can make an enormous difference. You'll see as you read on whether these steps are likely to be necessary for you. For some children, the positive response to Phase I is so powerful that the addition of the Consequences phase (Phase II) will be all that's needed to bring the child into her greatness and grow inner wealth.

All we really have is the present moment.
Every moment is an opportunity for transformation.
Get ready to learn to use these opportunities to form a new impression…

In a way, all we have is THIS MOMENT
And we will use these opportunities called MOMENTS to form a new impression…

Why Traditional Methods of Parenting Don't Work With Intense Children

Traditional methods of parenting *unwittingly reward or reinforce failure by way of giving energy to adverse or negative behaviors.* All too often, we end up trying to teach essential life lessons to children in moments when rules are being broken and when valued qualities like respect and responsibility are *not* being displayed. The idea is that if we are able to clearly communicate whatever notions will solve the problem at hand, we'll impart important learning. What ends up happening, though, is that the parent accidentally feeds the child's impression that she gets more out of life through negativity. On the flip side, the child receives much less energized relationship when she is *not* breaking rules or pushing boundaries. She ends up with a deepening impression that she gets more out of life through negativity.

When ordinary methods of teaching and parenting backfire, it's easy to feel as though it's your own fault. The child in question also ends up feeling ashamed and confused because he can't seem to resist going for the biggest possible hits of energy and connection – it's almost an addictive pattern. In truth, however, no one is to blame for the failures of the past. The real culprits are not parents, teachers or children. They are the methods we have at our disposal. To be successful, you must have the right tools for the job.

A Contrast in Tools: Traditional Methods and Nurtured Heart Methods

(OR: What IS Wrong as Opposed to What ISN'T Wrong)

Whether you believe in evolution or not, you have to admit that we wouldn't be here unless our ancestors had been good enough at avoiding danger to have survived. They couldn't wait until danger was upon them to fight or flee. In order to survive, they had to be observant enough to discern and process minute amounts of evidence, and then to be adept at sensing what might possibly be wrong with the picture of their surroundings. Traditional methods of parenting evolved from this survival skill.

Who couldn't walk into a child's room and immediately see things that could have been done better or that haven't been done at all? Our evolutionary experience has genetically engineered us to see tiny increments of what is wrong with the picture. And most of us can easily comment on these things at great length. In our culture, we have the language of failure down to a science. Most of us have the ability to wax poetic about what is wrong – for hours, if we feel that's the necessary time frame for a full explanation of every problem at hand.

Consider our culture's typical language of success. When we're pleased with something, we normally offer – at best – simple praises like "Good job!", "Thank you," or "Way to go." We tend to do that only when we are motivated by a sufficient amount of goodness, and we tend not to see tiny increments of success – let alone comment on them. As far as waxing poetic about what's going right, most of us fall short in that skill.

Add to this the fact that we only tend to see and comment on one side of the story: what has actually happened. How about what didn't happen that could have? How much, in every moment, does not go wrong? Any absence of negative outcomes can be held up as a success.

What are some things you are grateful for when they "aren't" happening?

If your child fusses, tantrums, or argues frequently, how do you feel when these behaviors are not occurring? Most likely, your primary feeling is relief. You probably don't want to rock the boat or give the child any ideas about bad behaviors he could be engaging in, but isn't. But there's a whole new dimension of success we can tap into through this lens – as long as you stay with the truth of any particular moment and let yourself feel genuine gratitude for the absence of problem behaviors:

"Jason, I really appreciate that you aren't arguing, throwing a tantrum or fussing. Thanks for following the rules and making good choices."

Compliments like this are far more powerful than "Thank you" or "Good job." Praises like these – or "Excellent!" "Great!" "Way to go!" – convey that you are pleased about something...but the child has no way of knowing what exactly they've done that is so great. Normal praise is inherently vague, and in this, it lacks power. The level of excitement typical of normal praise is far overshadowed by the energized intensity of the typical lecture, admonishment or warning.

Key Concept...

Catching Success vs. Creating Success

Almost every method of parenting and teaching suggests that adults "catch the child being good." With a challenging child, however, you might end up having to wait a long time for goodness to emerge. It's like trying to catch a dinosaur with a butterfly net: not the right tool for the job. The Nurtured Heart Approach is a tool that takes you out of the disempowered position of waiting for success. Instead, it equips you with techniques and attitudes that enable you to create success for the child.

At first glance, the concepts of catching success and creating success seem similar. They are actually very different. Catching success is about catching children in the act of doing something good, then complimenting them...usually with something like "Thank you" or "Good job!" There's nothing wrong with this, and it may bring some improvement, but it won't lead to the level of success needed for transformation – the shift that turns the worst kid on the block to the best kid on the block.

In creating success, we proactively orchestrate situations in which the child is irrefutably successful. We purposefully appreciate, recognize, acknowledge, celebrate, and applaud the child's efforts with big energy, connected relationship and elaborate detail. The child receives all the credit for having made the good choice.

Try This!

Experiment with creating success. Spend today challenging yourself to creatively pursue successful interventions with your challenging child. Notice how she responds to this new approach.

What Kind of Change Can I Expect to See

Every child is unique and will respond differently as you begin to use the techniques outlined in this book. Some might exhibit immediate outward change in response to your efforts. Some might pause, give you a quizzical look or say "Thank you." Others might not. Children's adverse behavior may actually worsen for a period of time as they test whether this new way of interacting is here to stay. Don't expect appreciation from the child right away. Continue to apply the techniques, knowing that over time you will see positive changes as inner wealth develops. The more the child needs this approach, the less likely you are to see immediate impact.

During the initial phases of refusal to energize negativity and super-energizing of success, rules will continue to be broken. This approach leaves the issue of consequences for broken rules out of the picture until Phase III, so you will need to continue to hold your child responsible for his actions in whatever way you normally have. Shift to enacting those consequences in as unceremonious and low-energy a fashion as possible. Skip all discussion, explanation and CSI (Crime Scene Investigation) in the aftermath of a consequence and get back to creating successes as quickly as possible. If you do lose your cool or resort to past ways of handling tense situations, give yourself credit for what you have achieved so far. Use your current frustration to muster more determination to use the new methodology to create next opportunities for success.

Learning a New Language

Have you ever learned a new language or traveled to a country where your language is not spoken? The process of adapting to a different culture can be unnerving and exhausting. If you're brave enough to speak the foreign language, you're likely to feel awkward at first. You might only know enough words on the first day to get yourself a cab and something to eat. By the end of the week, you may have several basic words and expressions under your belt, but you might still feel awkward. Only after several weeks or longer will you develop comfort and confidence in speaking the new language.

Learning the Nurtured Heart Approach is like learning a new language. At another level, it's like becoming steeped in a new culture. It's normal and natural for it to feel strange. You might experience anxiety or apprehension, just as you would when trying anything new and different. Honor your feelings and know that over time, you'll come to feel more comfortable. Accept that it won't feel natural for a while. Put your fear aside and just do it! Your trust in the approach and in yourself will grow as you begin to experience success.

Try This!

Think of a time this week when you could have made a fuss over something your child did…but you didn't go down that road. Imagine what you might have said or what your child might have said if you'd made the choice to focus on the problem. Take a moment, right now, to recognize your own greatness in not going there…in taking a stand not to energize negativity. Recall the moment. Give yourself some applause.

APPLAUSE, APPLAUSE, APPLAUSE….

The Timetable

As you learn the techniques of the Nurtured Heart Approach, we suggest that you introduce each technique for a period of a few days to a few weeks before moving on to the next one. The overall time to transformation will depend on the number of phases a given child needs and the level to which the old pattern has become entrenched. From our experience, most parents witness tremendously pleasing changes within a month; and by then, keeping it going feels easy. By this time, the techniques have become natural and spontaneous.

To make the most of this approach, apply the techniques with total commitment and all of your energy and intention. The mantra we suggest to make the most of it is: **"DO IT LIKE YOUR LIFE DEPENDS ON IT."** For now, give up any loyalties to other methods you've tried over the years. This approach works better if used on its own. So many other methods will be at cross-purposes and that will become increasingly apparent as you see your growing impact.

Single Parenting, Co-Parenting, and Everything in Between

Q: The Nurtured Heart Approach is a parenting approach. But what if you are divorced and in a co-parenting situation? How about single parenting altogether? Does the approach still work if you are the only one doing it?

A: The answer is a resounding **YES!** Any amount of emotional nutrition and positive interaction is beneficial to your child. While it is helpful to get all involved adults on the same page for consistency, The Nurtured Heart Approach can still be implemented if you must go it alone. If your partner is not on board with the approach, continue implementing and, chances are, when he/she sees the transformative benefits, he/she, too, will be a believer!

If you are co-parenting or in a shared custody arrangement, you can establish the approach while in your home and at school, regardless of whether both parents are participating. If the alternative household is in support of implementation, a parenting coach or therapist can be helpful in terms of working collaboratively with both households and all adults involved. Ideally, the approach is best implemented if all adults are on the same page. We have seen countless families, however, that have been profoundly changed when the approach has been implemented by only one parent.

As a single parent, using this approach with your intense child will make your role as the sole disciplinarian easier because your child will take on more responsibility for her choices and develop inner wealth commensurate with increased self-confidence and independence. You will find you have more time to enjoy each other and less time in "survival mode." Even though you may have more on your plate, by using The Nurtured Heart Approach, your parenting job becomes easier. You no longer have to legislate by committee. You get to decide what you want for your family and you get to create what it looks like!

The Wrap Up

In this chapter, you learned some basics about what this approach is, what it aims to achieve, and where it came from. You've developed:

- Insight about why children, particularly intense children, feed on the negative emotional energy they receive, and why they behave as they do – because they are acting out of their negative portfolio.

- An understanding of why your efforts might not have been successful in the past, and that you are not to blame – because typical tools have proven minimally useful with challenging children.

- A knowledge that your fear about using new tools is normal and natural, and that immediate outward change may not happen – but that transformation will come with time and dedicated application.

- A basic understanding that the Nurtured Heart Approach works by changing a child's negative portfolio into a positive one – by creating honest experiences of success that, over time, create inner wealth and transform behaviors.

- An assurance that even if you're the only parent in the child's life who is working with this approach, you can implement this approach with wonderful success.

The Next Step

We're ready to move on to the first and most important phase of the Nurtured Heart Approach: a refusal to energize the negative plus strategies for energizing success. But first, let's review a few crucial notions.

CHAPTER 1

Crucial Concepts of
The Nurtured Heart Approach

In order to bring the methods of The Nurtured Heart Approach to life, we need to share two crucial concepts. These are simple ideas, but if you implement them successfully, you will feel in your bones both the problem with typical methods and exactly what it is that you need to accomplish. THEN the techniques of The Nurtured Heart Approach will make total sense.

Concept 1: Toys Are Us

We are by far a child's most interesting "toy." We have many more features – actions, reactions and moods – than any other toy in their collection. We are the ultimate entertainment center.

Think for a moment about how children are when they receive a new toy. They check it out and are likely to find that this toy, like all toys, has features. It might be two or two thousand features. Hopefully, the child will find some aspects compelling; however, the child might find some features to be boring. Those are the ones that children rarely return to. Maybe they will try again, just to see whether it has changed. But once they determine a feature to be predictably boring, they write it off and don't go back.

How about us as toys? How many features do we have? Most of us are capable of a zillion actions and movements. It doesn't take long for a difficult child to realize that he can "push our buttons" and generate a wide array of emotions, moods, sounds, or animation. And how much more interesting that "toy" becomes when things are going wrong!

Children continually form impressions of how the world works and of the impact they have on their surroundings. They discover through interactions that they can have an impact on another's response. Children are fascinated by our reactions and their *ability to engage our animation.*

A "difficult child" – one who is more needy, sensitive and intense than a "normal" child – when exposed to conventional ways of parenting, can easily develop the impression that this "toy" (us) is much more animated, interesting, exciting, responsive and emotional when she (the child) exhibits poor choices and unacceptable behaviors. This child can also conclude that the "toy" is far less interesting and relatively boring when things are going right. She can come to "write us off" for the low-key responses she receives for her good choices, and she can decide to "accelerate" her instances of poor behavior because it generates so much more attention and reaction from the "toy."

Children take note of just what it takes to REALLY get us going

Children experience the absolute underlying truth of what brings forth our aliveness and connection. Challenging children are drawn to more intense reactions, and they decode information in different ways than we imagine.

They carefully track adults' investment of time, energy and attention and can perceive it as what we love and celebrate. This investment is like a river that runs beneath the words we say and the things we do. Children want to be where that river flows most strongly. With standard parenting methods, this river flows most mightily when things are going wrong. Urgent attempts at breakthrough communication in moments where rules are being broken – through lectures, discussions and words of wisdom – end up reinforcing exactly what we don't want.

While we desperately hope children will respond to these messages that are typically wrapped in logic, reason and rational urgency, in the process of delivering our sermon, we *accidentally* wind up feeding the child's impression that he gets more through adversity. That is because we are energetically *delivering more relationship at the wrong time and for the wrong reason.*

The 100 Dollar Bills

Basically, we are energetically giving out stacks of hundred-dollar bills when things are going wrong. No one would do that on purpose, but inadvertently, just by following typical parenting recommendations, we wind up doing that all the time.

Our emotions, reactions, energy and relationship are the prize, and children, particularly challenging children, have an uncanny way of knowing where "more" of the prize is. If we offered you a $5 or a $50 bill, which would you pick? How long did it take you to determine you could acquire more with a $50 bill? Do you think children are any less tuned in to where MORE is?

They have learned that they get more energy from us when things are going wrong – that *they get more out of life through adversity.* Conversely, they also have figured out that doing the occasional "right" thing generates a much more boring response, if any.

The Prize

IT'S WORTH REPEATING: Our emotions, our responses, our level of involvement, our energies are the prize. If an intense child comes to believe that he can get greater payoffs for negative behaviors, he will repeat that pattern over and over. He is not out to "get us," but he is out to get our energy.

Toys Are Us ...

We are by far our children's favorite toy. Think about what happens when children get a new toy. They are not likely to say, "Thanks, I'll come back later." They want to explore the toy. They want to dive in.

No matter what the toy is, children seem naturally drawn to features they find most exciting, animated and compelling. Those are the features they return to, over and over. And they seldom go back to the boring features.

Adults have many more features than the ordinary toy - more actions, emotions and moods. We're the ultimate entertainment center...remote control included!

Think about the way your child may see you as a toy. What are your most intriguing features? How does your child get the "bells and whistles" going? Is the energy of your responses relatively low key and boring when things are going right?

If this "Toys Are Us" concept resonates with you, chances are you are well on your way to creating a great outcome. With this new understanding, the techniques are going to fall into place. The "light bulb going on" moment you are having right now will propel you into the techniques of this approach in a clear and definite way.

We applaud YOU for your openness to new concepts and ideas! We know with a strong degree of certainty from our work with families that, when this concept makes sense, everything else seems to fall into place fairly easily.

The Questions

How much energy are we radiating? To what extent? And for what?

In truth, we may not have a choice **not** to be a favorite "toy" in the mind of the child; in fact, many of us might actually cherish that role. But what kind of toy are we going to be? Fortunately, we get to choose how, when and to what extent we radiate. This makes all the difference in the world!

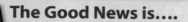

The Good News is....

We get to decide WHAT we radiate, HOW we radiate, and TO WHAT DEGREE we radiate.

An Experiment with Radiation

Decide to radiate positive energy for the rest of the day. Challenge yourself to be a beacon of light for every person you encounter. Refuse to give your energy to what you DON'T want. Begin with being conscious of your body language and facial expressions. Challenge yourself to compliment people around you honestly; just notice one thing they are doing that is positive and comment on it as specifically as possible. For example, one of the authors (Joann) noticed that a U.S. Postal Service clerk saw that the line at the post office was lengthening considerably, and she opened an extra window to allow the waiting people a chance to complete their transactions sooner. Joann happily commented to that clerk about her positive action, indicating how much she appreciated the clerk's thoughtful gesture. The clerk beamed!

So, experiment today with the ways **you** elaborate and **you** make these moments of appreciation more energized and authentic!

At the end of your day, take a moment to jot down a few of your experiences. How did people respond? Did you notice a change as you interacted in these energized and more appreciative ways?

_____

_____

_____

_____

_____

_____

_____

_____

Applaud yourself!

With each and every step, you are actively moving in the direction of transformation

Concept 2: Video Game Therapy

It is not an accident that children are attracted to games like Nintendo.

Typically, when parents seek help with their child, it is associated with poor focus and choices at home and at school. We have often heard comments like this: "Why is it that my child can be doing so poorly, yet when he's playing one of his video games, he has never-ending concentration and is at his best? When he's playing these games, he's so good at getting the goals and not breaking the rules. Why can't he do that at home or school?"

The answer is that video games have the perfect level of structure, and they always deliver. While the child is playing the video game, life truly makes sense. The **rules** are totally clear and predictable, and so are the **incentives**. The positives and the limits are in the right places and at the right levels. While the child is playing one of these games – working toward the goals, achieving the goals, and not breaking the rules – the game is essentially in his face, confronting him with profound evidence of success. That success takes the form of **energy** such as bells and whistles and scoring. The game is **IN THE NOW,** responding to whatever is the truth. At any moment, if the child makes a mistake, the game is still in the truth of the moment and gives notification of a consequence. The flow of energy is always congruent with the truth of the moment. In short, the game *always delivers*. The child cannot talk or manipulate his way out of the situation. No excuses work. He simply gets a consequence for his act or choice, and then it's over and he's right back to the next moment, when, if played right, the game makes a *big deal* over the successes.

Life as a Video Game?

- In video games, life makes total sense.

- The rules are clear and predictable.

- The game provides perfect structure and clear, consistent consequences at every level of play.

- The game doesn't lecture, scold or otherwise give energy to mistakes or broken rules.

- The child knows what to do to score, score, score!

- He becomes expert at **<u>NOT</u>** breaking the rules.

- The game is **ALWAYS** in the **NOW.**

In video games, the payoff is NOT upside down.

In video games, the payoff of energy is not *upside down*. The consequences are virtually nothing – almost an illusion. Adults looking at these games think the consequences are drastic and punitive – heads rolling, blood spurting and so forth. But the player is back in the game in mere seconds. And these games have ingenious ways of creating and rewarding success, thereby encouraging it. Somehow this structure conspires to help children be consistently talented, focused and motivated. Given the right level of structure, these children can really play to win. The structure helps them use their intensity and energies successfully. The good news is that they can apply themselves to **LIFE** with the same zeal.

Conventional models of teaching and disciplining have major structural problems – they are upside down!

In traditional methods of parenting, the limits and incentives are *upside down*. The energy from adults is greater when things are going wrong, and what we think are limits are often actually rewards. The energy for positive behaviors is often modest in comparison to the responses to adversity. Simply put, we radiate more energy when a child is misbehaving than when she is behaving appropriately – even while issuing consequences! If actions truly speak louder than words, we often wind up showing children more "love" when adversity IS happening than when it ISN'T happening. We are so much more willing to give more time, relationship and response at those moments. **This is upside down!** In reality, we are *rewarding the very opposite of what we want to reward*. The child ends up confused about what's a consequence and what's a reward.

The Library Story

Howard Glasser happened to be in a school library setting up for a presentation. Since it was still during school hours, librarians as well as students were in other areas of the room. The librarians were working while the children were engaged in their own activities. Suddenly a minor disruption among the children prompted one librarian to go over and motion for a boy to come and talk to her.

The librarian, clearly a kind and caring person, sweetly put her arm around this disruptive boy and began a little discussion of what he should and should not do in the future. She continued this for a minute or so, and then she asked the student to go back to his table. Within minutes, not only was he disruptive again, but several other children joined in the fray.

When reviewing the above story, you may be asking yourself, "What is the problem with the way the librarian handled it?" Actually there were two problems: the librarian's timing was awful, and she was inadvertently rewarding the problem behavior.

To the extent that she discussed the problem with the boy at that moment of adversity, she was emanating energy, relationship and life force at the *wrong time*. She was actually *rewarding* the problem behavior. While she was **saying** "Don't do that again," at the very same time she was giving the student, in terms of *energy,* a stack of hundred dollar bills. That certainly wasn't her intention; however, this is an extremely common reason why normal approaches backfire. They are **upside down!**

We certainly prefer that the librarian be loving and kind; however, she will have optimal impact when the kind and loving words flow for **SUCCESSES**.

When problems happen, we will recommend a simple, effective consequence that involves almost no words.

Traditional methods of parenting aren't nearly as clear or powerful or encompassing to the child as video games.

Even though we personally may not like that these games are often violent and inane, they manage to exert a very clear and guiding force field on the domain the child enters into when playing them.

The **GOOD NEWS** is that this "video game" thinking and way of operating are totally transposable to all of the other environments in which children exist – school, home, social situations and so forth. And, given the right guidance, children will respond by quickly becoming equally as sensational in real life as they are when playing these games.

AND the **GREAT NEWS** is, from this point of view, there is **NO BLAME.** The teacher isn't the culprit, the parent isn't the culprit, nor is the child the culprit.

Instead, the culprits are the methods we have at our disposal. Conventional approaches almost always tell us to exert energy and relationship when things are going wrong. Children often wind up confused as to whether something was an incentive or whether it was a consequence.

It therefore is no surprise that too many children are diagnosed with disorders (and subsequently medicated). Was it really pathology, like ADHD, if one month later the child is using her intensity in wonderful ways?

As parents, teachers, or therapists, all that any of us are seeking is an approach that works. When things aren't going well, most of us feel awful, responsible and guilty.

You now know that it isn't you – it's the methods that have been at fault. But if you turn to a method that works, you become a hero. And ultimately, you will produce children who are heroes.

The Wrap Up

So, now you know about the "simple ideas" of Energizing Success.

- You understand that children are in the process of learning that they can have an impact on others by what they do, that we are our children's favorite toy, and that children desire our **energy** as a response to their behavior.

- You know that some children in particular have learned that they receive more of our energy for poor choices and unacceptable behaviors than for good choices and acceptable behaviors, and you are aware that they have learned they get more out of life through adverse behavior.

- You understand that children perform well when the payoff is right side up and not upside down. They do best when life makes sense; they thrive when rules are clear and predictable; and they respond best to minimal consequences and energized rewards for success.

- You have noted that our traditional methods of teaching and parenting are often upside down, inadvertently rewarding negativity – the very opposite of what we want to do – so that the child ends up confused about what's a consequence and what's a reward.

- You have noted that we **can** change the way we radiate energy. We **can** change the upside down to right side up by giving our energy to positive behaviors. We **can** energize success rather than failure.

- Please understand that we are *not* recommending video games, but we *are* recommending the underlying structure of those games.

The Next Step

But first, before we go on, there are some stands we need to take within ourselves to produce change. We are now ready to appreciate those stands.

Taking Stands That Will Produce Change

In order to produce change, it is essential that you take three stands throughout the process.

STAND #1: Absolutely No! I refuse to energize negative behavior. I refuse to be drawn into giving the child greater responses, animation and "payoff" for negative behaviors. I will not accidentally foster failures and reward problems by responding with my energy and relationship. I will not accidentally energize negativity. (There will be consequences for negative behaviors, but all my energy will go toward energizing success.)

STAND #2: Absolutely Yes! I resolve to relentlessly energize the positive. I will strategically pull the child into a new pattern of success. I will see and express greatness and consistently and often confront my child with his/her successes.

STAND #3: Absolute Clarity! I will maintain total clarity about rules that demonstrate fair and consistent boundaries and consequences: a simple matter of "Here are the rules, and here's what happens when you break one." I resolve to give a true, effective consequence when a rule is broken. Immediately after the consequence ends, I will once again begin energizing successes.

We think you will be very pleasantly surprised to find out just how effective a simple but true consequence can be. (**BUT,** please do not jump ahead at this point because, as essential as consequences are to the transformation process, *beginning* with consequences is a mistake.)

Please let us explain. Most parents of difficult children are typically advised to emphasize rules and consequences as a first line of improvement. In our experience, this is like trying to put a second floor on a home that doesn't yet have a foundation and first floor. It will backfire.

In the Nurtured Heart Approach, the foundation is a staunch refusal to energize negativity. The first floor is the relentless energizing of success.

We will discuss limit-setting thoroughly and we will fully explain the timing of perfect consequences later in this workbook when the stage is set for them to have transformative impact.

For now, simply continue to employ whatever consequences you've used in the past, but give them as little of your energy and passion as possible. Drain them of all drama. Refuse to take the bait when your child gives you a chance to pour your precious energy, connectedness and relationship into responding to negative behaviors. Focus on the **Absolute No** in engaging your ability to not give energy to negativity and the **Absolute Yes** of your ability to energize the positive.

What is a Stand?

Taking a stand is maintaining a belief in an unbending and courageous way. We take a stand when we reach a point of clarity and resolve. **Failure is not an option.** Think about the stands you have taken in your life. The fact that you are reading this book indicates that you have decided to find another way to parent your child. In all probability, you reached a point of clarity and resolve that the old methods were not working for you.

The Nurtured Heart Approach recommends that you take three specific Stands from this point forward. They are:

1. **I REFUSE to be drawn into accidentally energizing and rewarding negativity.**

2. **I WILL purposefully create successes for my child.**

3. **I WILL provide a TRUE consequence when a rule is broken.**

Taking a Stand

When do you take a stand? What do you feel VERY strongly about? Religion? Politics? Child Rearing? Human Rights? We all have things we feel very strongly about. What are some things that come to mind for you?

_____

_____

_____

_____

_____

_____

_____

_____

_____

Phase I Exercises

Phase I of the Nurtured Heart Approach consists of REFUSING TO ENERGIZE NEGATIVITY while PURPOSEFULLY CHOOSING TO ENERGIZE SUCCESS (in other words, Stands 1 and 2). Below are three practice scenarios.

1. Imagine that your intense child is in the midst of a battle with his brother. They have been bickering all morning and finally came to you to solve the problem. You notice that your child has somehow managed not to hit his brother and, although he appears to be extremely frustrated, he remains receptive to solving the problem. What might be the best response in light of the three Stands?

    A. Lecture him about how disrespectful it is to argue with his brother.

    B. Tell both children to go to their rooms to cool down.

    C. Ignore the situation and walk away.

    D. **Tell your child, "Thanks for not taking your anger out on anyone. That's really good self-control. I also notice that you decided to solve the problem in a safe way. I am so proud of you for asking for help and managing such intense feelings well."**

Why is response "D" the best choice? Pay attention to how this choice serves to energize success and how it refuses to fall into the trap of energizing negativity. Can you think of any additional appreciative comments that could have been said?

_____

_____

_____

_____

Here's another example of taking both Stands together. As long as the child's behavior DOES NOT cross the line and as long as rules ARE NOT BEING BROKEN, the child is "in the game," and strategies to create successes and avoid giving energy to negativity are vital. If the line IS crossed at any point, give a consequence but no energy to the problem (remain neutral). This will be explained thoroughly later in the book.

2. It's a school day and your family is in the kitchen for breakfast. Your intense child happens to be a morning grump, but this morning she has not instigated any arguments with anyone. Although she mumbles under her breath about how she hates cold cereal, she continues to slowly eat. What might be the best response in light of the Phase I stands?

    A. Make her something else for breakfast, hoping to avoid a blowup.

    B. Break into a lecture about how there are starving children in the world.

    C. Order her to leave the table until she changes her attitude.

    D. **Tell her, "I notice that you got up on your own so nicely this morning, and even though you are not happy with your breakfast, you are still eating it. I also notice how well you have been taking care of your frustration this morning because I know how hard that can be."**

Why is response "D" the best choice? Pay attention to how this choice serves to energize success and how it refuses to fall into the trap of energizing negativity. How does this resonate with your personal experiences? What would help you remember to take this new stand?

_____

_____

_____

_____

Remember the two stands of Phase I: I refuse to reward negativity with my energy, response and relationship – AND I resolve to purposefully create opportunities to recognize my child's success.

3. Your 13-year-old enters the room with a "chip on his shoulder." He has been arguing with his brother and comes to you to complain about how much he hates sharing a room. You notice that this time he stopped the arguing before it got physical and he is now coming to you for help to solve the problem. What might be the best response in light of Phase I stands?

    A. Try to change the subject and cheer him up.

    B. Give him a lecture about how you can't afford a bigger house, so he's just going to have to get along.

    C. Tell him that you will talk to his brother about staying out of his things.

    D. **Say, "I see how powerful you are being in handling this difficult situation. You did not lash out, you did not curse, and now you are trying to solve the problem in a calm manner. That's excellent! That shows me your inner wisdom and good judgment."**

Why is response "D" the best choice? Pay attention to how this choice serves to energize success and how it refuses to fall into the trap of energizing negativity. Jot down any thoughts that would be helpful to you in situations like this.

_____

_____

_____

_____

_____

Phase II Exercises

Phase II of The Nurtured Heart Approach consists of SETTING CLEAR AND CONSISTENT LIMITS AND CONSEQUENCES while simultaneously REFUSING TO ENERGIZE NEGATIVITY. (In other words, Stands 2 and 3.) Before we explain the Phase II strategies, here are two illustrations of those all-important Stands.

1. Your child interrupts you in a disrespectful manner while you are talking on the phone. What might be the best response in light of the Phase II Stands?

   A. You end the call and begin a discussion with your child about how inappropriate her behavior is.

   B. You raise your voice and in a firm manner tell her to not be disrespectful.

   C. Yell that there will be no phone privileges for her for one week.

   D. **Tell her, "That's a consequence." Then enact the brief consequence, after which you recognize her for doing her consequence well. You then compliment her for NOW not interrupting and for NOW not being disrespectful.**

When done properly, short consequences are the perfect background for creating even more first-hand experiences of success. Response "D" also serves to let the child see that the parent didn't accidentally energize negativity but did, indeed, enact a consequence with no fanfare. Remember how short the consequences are in video games? Yet, they are amazingly effective.

Another way of framing the consequence Stand is to think of it as: "Here are the rules and here are the consequences for breaking a rule. I will no longer look the other way and I will always give a TRUE consequence." A big component of how a consequence really becomes TRUE is to REFUSE to accidentally give energy to the negativity while administering the consequence. This helps the child see that he has received a TRUE result for having broken a rule, but that the adverse behavior is not paying off in negative energy. It is truly a matter of perception. The child ABSOLUTELY needs to see that there is a result for having broken a rule. **However,** *it is not how PUNITIVE a consequence is that matters. What we are fighting for is to awaken the child to his SUCCESSFULNESS.*

The truth is…every time your child is NOT engaging in negative behavior, he IS being successful.

2. Your child doesn't take "no" for an answer when you are eating out and he asks for more dessert. He fusses, whines and argues that it's not fair. Which might seem to be the best response in light of the Phase II Stands?

A. You immediately request the check and leave the restaurant as quickly as possible.

B. You sternly threaten that he will never have dessert again if he doesn't stop fussing immediately.

C. You tell him you are getting mad and that it's not okay to be demanding and not okay to have second helpings of sweets.

D. **You immediately give him a short time-out by saying, "That's a consequence." Then you quickly tell him the consequence is over, thanking him for doing his consequence well and for NOW not fussing and for NOW not whining or arguing. (By the way, he still doesn't get the second helping.)**

At this point, we have not yet given you strategies for enacting consequences. You may be asking, "And how do you expect my son to simply agree to his time-out consequence?" as in the example above. Fear not, we will cover consequences in detail, but know for now that, in the scene above, response "D" is the one that will work to bring about your child's transformation.

First-Hand vs. Second-Hand Experiences...or Right Side Up, Not Upside Down

First-hand experiences of success reflect back to the child that she really is having a positive impact upon others and that her life has meaning. Traditional ways of parenting in our society have led us to teach many lessons through second-hand experiences. For example, we expose our children to ideas about morals and values through books, movies, lectures and discussions. Rather than teaching the child important positive morals through **her own** direct experience, we rely on teaching her these ideas in an indirect, second-hand way through **our** experience. The truth is that second-hand experiences have less of an impact. Further, second-hand experiences risk the possibility of backfiring.

In addition, the only time we ordinarily provide first-hand experience relating specifically to what the child is doing is when things are going WRONG. Take our lectures about values such as respect and responsibility. When are they usually delivered? When things are going wrong, not when they are going right. Our society has led us to believe that we can teach values and morals in a straightforward and logical way and has us trying to accomplish this at the very *wrong* moment in time. Unfortunately, this backfires because the lectures become powerful first-hand evidence of failure, essentially saying to the child, "Here you are being celebrated energetically for your lack of responsibility." Again, this is **upside down.** For the difficult child, this will only serve to deepen his impression that he gets more out of life through adversity.

In contrast, we need to provide honest, powerful first-hand experiences whereby we celebrate important qualities by taking advantage of all the moments at our disposal when the adversity is **not** happening – when things are going right! So why not actively use strategies that capture moments in an absolutely *truthful manner* – in a manner that absolutely reflects to the child that she is celebrated for her decisions, judgment and wisdom? Avoid altogether the issue of whether she can or can't manifest a particular quality; instead, let her know "she is" because here she is **NOW** successfully doing it. This is *right side up, not upside down!*

Honest First-hand Experiences of Success Build a Positive Portfolio

Taking advantage of all the moments at our disposal when adversity is **not** happening communicates to the child the experience of first-hand success, which in turn gradually begins to build his positive portfolio and subsequently provides him a powerful inner experience of his real wealth.

It is not at all difficult to help a child have a first-hand experience of his greatness and divine nature when we provide evidence that focuses upon his positive behaviors at any given point in time. If we have a way of capturing those moments, then we can have a great deal of influence in broadening his inner wealth.

"Here you are RIGHT NOW being great. Thanks for choosing to be prepared for class today and for choosing to have a great attitude."

"Here you are RIGHT NOW being great. You got your homework done, you completed your chores and you didn't even have to be reminded."

First-hand experience vs. Second-hand experience: An Example

A boy arrived home from school. At the bottom of his backpack was a crumpled green piece of paper. It was a note from a teacher praising him for demonstrating the pillars of character from the "Character Counts" curriculum that is taught in many of the schools in Arizona.

When asked what it was for, he said that he was not really sure, but he knew it "must have been something good." The fact that it was found at the bottom of his backpack suggests that, on some level, it failed to impress him. It had not registered as success in a clear and tangible way. While the intent was to praise him, this second-hand experience did not override his defensive radar. **If we were to rewind the tape and recognize him in the moment, it would have had a much more intense, "first-hand experience" effect.**

Here's an example of how we can "wrap" the intended success around an actual "irrefutable" experience: *"Daniel, I appreciate the good attitude you are using right now in the way you are listening and contributing to our discussion. You are adding to what we know."*

A First-Hand Experience of Success

Creating opportunities to energize success allows the child to actually experience being capable. These created opportunities speak to the truth that "It's not a question of whether you can or can't – you ARE being successful."

The Nurtured Heart Approach strategies create a scenario in which you "accuse" the child of success on a daily basis – almost like a positive confrontation: "Here's how I see you being successful right this second."

"Tom, I'm appreciating your choice to get along with your sister. Thanks for being considerate."

"Sarah, thanks for handling your frustration well. I know you wanted a second helping of dessert and were mad when I said no, but I am so proud of you for not arguing or fussing."

These appreciative comments are the truth and in the here and now – regardless of past or future problems.

Now the question is, how do we go about creating first-hand, honest success experiences for the child? The answer is that we need ways to **see** and **say things** in a manner that multiplies the effect.

To help you understand this, next we'll provide two teaching stories that relay the intention that supercharges every aspect of the Nurtured Heart Approach. Then, we'll move on to techniques.

Essential Intentions that Energize Success

The Shamu Story.

Shamu, a 19,000-pound whale, along with others of his kind, has awed many audiences by his ability to leap over a rope stretched high above his tank. How did Shamu learn to do this trick? The secret was in his trainers' approach. The trainers "cheated" by starting with the rope at the bottom of the tank. **IN THAT WAY THE TRAINERS CREATED A SCENARIO WHERE THE ONLY OUTCOME COULD BE SUCCESS.**

To begin with, Shamu simply swam, allowing the trainers all the time in the world to notice his approaching success and to give pats, recognition and other appreciation for actually swimming over the rope. By virtue of how his trainers "tricked" him into being successful, Shamu learned that *every time he swam over the rope he was highly energized.* Once they saw that Shamu had made the connection between the rope and the sense of success, the trainers simply kept raising the rope a little higher at each training session. Shamu's trainers, in essence, "hijacked" him into success. We all like high expectations, but had they started with the rope up at 25 feet, the training process would never have had a chance.

Shamu

- How do they get a two-ton whale to jump so high?

- They create successes that would not otherwise exist.

- They base the relationship and focus ONLY on the positive.

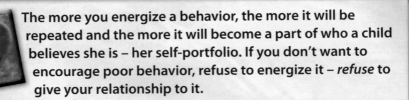

The more you energize a behavior, the more it will be repeated and the more it will become a part of who a child believes she is – her self-portfolio. If you don't want to encourage poor behavior, refuse to energize it – *refuse* to give your relationship to it.

Like Shamu, with our children we need a mindset and an intention that helps us create successes that would not otherwise exist.

By **restructuring our idea of what success is,** we can "trick" or "hijack" our children into being successful. We can then provide positive, first-hand experience of *who they really are.*

Once the child understands the link between the internal feeling of success and your response in terms of energy and relationship, he will begin to seek and integrate success into every aspect of life. Here are a few examples of how this intention leads to appreciative statements:

"Desmond, I love how thoughtful and considerate you are being to your sister by letting her concentrate on her homework. Thanks for choosing not to disturb her. I really like how great you are in showing her you care."

"Thanks for being so helpful, Emily. I appreciate how kind and loving you have been to the dogs. They are trusting you so much more now that you are feeding and brushing them consistently and playing with them in nicer ways."

David is a wonderful, real-life example of this principle. David was an extremely defiant six-year-old whose parents were entirely frustrated in their attempts to gain compliance. During his father's initial visit with Howard Glasser, Dad was simply told: "For now, be as clever and as simple in your requests as possible to get the successes going. That's the secret." (Remember SHAMU!)

David's father had to leave Glasser's office to pick his son up at school. He returned later with a broad smile on his face. It appeared he had accomplished his mission. When asked how, with great pride the father reported that David had climbed into the car and was in the act of closing the door when his father requested: "David, I need you to close the door."

It was, of course, already a done deal, and all that was left was to congratulate David for following directions, which was done in an excellent fashion. Following that, several other exceedingly doable requests yielded the same kind of outcome. The family was on its way, and within a relatively short time, David was predominantly cooperative with both simple and more complex requests, and his parents were quite pleased with the change.

The Shamu story reminds us to start with the rope at the bottom of the tank.

David's parents abandoned all of the methods they'd already tried for parenting a difficult child. This was brilliant. They began anew by making their requests as simple as necessary to foster compliance. Despite their anger over years of defiance, they were willing to be appreciative of even the smallest successes. They brilliantly created successes that would otherwise not have existed. They created tasks at which it was virtually impossible for David to fail.

Over the next few days, experiment *yourself* with making some "ridiculously" simple and doable requests. As each is completed, purposefully applaud the success with more detail than ever before. Remember, it's so easy in our society for adults to go on and on when something is done wrong, so try going on and on for something done right.

For example: "Jose, I really like that you followed my directions and held the door for me. That was very helpful. What I liked best was that you listened to my request and did exactly what I asked you to do."

The Tollbooth Attendant:
It's all in how we CHOOSE to see things.

The story has been told of an Oakland Bay Bridge tollbooth attendant. A driver on his morning commute was approaching the tollbooth, and upon rolling down his window, he heard rock-and-roll dance music blaring from a radio nearby. Looking around, he noted a tollbooth attendant in his cubicle a few lanes away grooving to the beat and having a great time. Curious, the driver purposely pulled into that lane and said to the attendant, "It looks as if you're having a great time."

The tollbooth attendant responded, "Of course! I'm having a party. I have the best job in the world and the best office in the world." The driver inquired as to what that meant. The attendant replied, "Well, I get to be out here listening to my favorite tunes, doing my own thing and meeting nice people. Besides, what executive do you know who has an office with four glass walls and a view that even comes close to this one? I can look west and just about see the ocean. I can look north and south and see beautiful views of the bay, and I can look east and see the mainland. If I work the early shift, I can see the sunrise. If I work later, I can see the sunset. With all these clouds the view is different every day. Nothing can compare to this. Besides, I'm going to be a dancer, and I'm getting paid to practice."

The driver then pointed to the other tollbooths and said, "What about the other attendants? They don't seem to be having the time of their lives." The tollbooth attendant looked him in the eyes and replied, "Oh, those guys in the stand-up coffins…they're no fun."

Everything is subject to how we choose to view it.

The moral of this story is that we can create successes *by the way we choose to see things*. No matter what has already transpired, *we get to choose, moment to moment*. Is the glass half-full or is it half-empty? We can choose to see things in the tollbooth attendant's upbeat fashion without ever departing from the absolute truth of a given moment.

It is like pointing a camera, taking a picture and simply saying out loud the truth of the moment the camera captured. In The Nurtured Heart Approach there is never a need to say anything that is not true. But by way of how we choose to view it – our intentions – we can access levels of truth beyond options available in the past.

"Carlos, the truth of what I see right now is that you are making a successful decision to focus on your chores even though I know you'd rather be playing with your friends. Thanks so much for helping out."

"Amanda, you are being so cooperative with your friends this afternoon by sharing so well and by letting them have a turn choosing the games you are playing. That is so respectful."

Just stay in the moment and create the successes!

The Heart of Creating Success is our Attitude... Our Intention

Whether or not we opt to see successes is our choice. We get to choose at any given moment how we are going to view the world and the everyday events in it that comprise our lives and the life of our child. The questions then are, "Can we come up with an approach that capitalizes on these intentions?" "Can we find an approach that greatly enhances the opportunity to create within our children deeper experiences of success than other methods normally promote?"

The answer is that simply by bringing the lessons of Shamu and the Tollbooth Attendant to this endeavor, we *can create successes that would not otherwise exist* and we *can create successes by the way we choose to see things*. The Nurtured Heart Approach's strategies do precisely that.

In the next chapter we will begin teaching you the methods designed to strategically create and energize success. They must go hand-in-hand, however, with your constant refusal to accidentally energize negativity.

This refusal to energize the negative might seem simple at first, but it can be the most difficult part of learning and practicing this approach. Difficult children who know exactly how to push our buttons will go to great lengths to try to get you to energize their negative choices: to bring you back into the kind of relationship they're used to, and that they know backward and forward.

When you feel yourself tempted to go to that place, take a moment. Try a few deep breaths or give yourself a cue to step back and disengage to a sense of being unplugged or reset. Instead of thinking in the old terms – "I can't let this slide! I have to stomp out this bad behavior!" – think in terms of saying "no thank you" to something you don't want more of…just as you'd do if someone brought you a plate of food you didn't want. When it comes to interacting with children it's counterintuitive for most of us, but it's essential for the success of this approach. And if you fall off that horse, it's okay; we all do! Just return to your stand to refuse to energize negativity from that moment forward.

Until we introduce the consequence phase, if your child breaks a rule, we suggest that you simply administer whatever consequences you used in the past, but do so without any explanation, discussion, sermons, emotion, energy or relationship. Experiment with keeping the consequence simple and short so it can be over quickly and you can purposefully move right back to creating successes. If you are dying to impart a "lesson" to the child, embed it in a new success once the consequence is complete. For example: *"Carly, thanks for choosing to not argue and tantrum right now. It really feels peaceful when you make the choice you are making right now."*

Intention Meets Trajectory

At a recent gathering at a Greek restaurant in Tucson, we had a first hand experience of creating intention and trajectory. The restaurant owner was explaining why it is customary in the Greek culture to throw plates on the ground. He said, "It is very simple. I break a plate and tomorrow I go to the store and replace it with another. You are a human being. My love for you is irreplaceable." He then pointed to one of the women in our group and told her she needed to try it. She became flustered and said, "There is no way – I can't." He said, "I will help you," and he stood next to her to coach her through it. He explained that all she had to do was throw it in the air. She kept shaking her head and saying, "I can't do it, I can't do it." Eventually, she mustered up her courage and began to throw the plate. It flew high into the air. It hit the window and landed on the floor, completely unscathed. We all looked in disbelief at what had just happened.

The restaurant owner looked at her and said, "Now that you have practiced, let's do it again." He stood next to her and continued to encourage her. She pulled herself together and said out loud, "Okay, I am ready." She proceeded to throw the plate. Again it flew into the air and this time it smashed into several pieces on the ground. The woman looked at the shattered ceramic shards in disbelief and then at the restaurant owner. He looked at the woman tenderly and said, "Just breathe it in." After a moment, the woman said, "My God, you just changed my life!" She took with her a piece of the plate to remind her of this experience.

From this story, you see that the woman had a first-hand experience of initially creating an intention and then a trajectory. At first, when she believed she could not throw the plate, even though she wanted to, she was not able to break the plate. Initially the intention was there, but not the trajectory. The second time around, when her intention was in line with her trajectory, she was able to break the plate. The moral of this story is: We can have all the good intentions in the world, but if we do not create, through our attitudes, responses and perceptions, a clear path upon which the intentions will travel, at the end of the day all we have are good intentions.

The 3 Intentions

In The Nurtured Heart Approach, we keep in mind the following intentions:

1. **To help kids feel GREAT about who they are.**

2. **To CREATE SUCCESSES that would not otherwise exist. (Shamu)**

3. **To become adept at IDENTIFYING WHAT IS RIGHT with the picture. (Toll Taker)**

The Wrap Up

Now we know that in order to produce change, we need to take a firm internal stand to refuse to energize negativity; to relentlessly energize successes; and to impose a clear, simple consequence when a rule is broken.

- Always start with the first and second Stands to create honest and truthful success experiences. Why? These experiences help to develop the child's new positive portfolio. Once this portfolio begins to develop, the child is launched on the path toward transformation.

- Remember to initiate the process of energizing success with the mindset of Shamu's trainers, by first making requests as simple as they need to be (rope at the bottom of the tank) to produce a repetitive pattern of successes. Then work gradually from there.

- View the everyday life experiences of the child in a truthfully positive light (as in the story of the tollbooth attendant) and observe the successes you did not even realize existed. Resolve to *create* success experiences in each moment.

The Next Step

Now that these principles are firmly in your grasp, we are ready to move on to the specific techniques that energize success. We liken these techniques to the processes of a camera because we think of them as ways of capturing moments in the mind's eye and reflecting them back to the child. We can be as creative as we want in the process. It's almost like handing a photograph to the child of herself, being undeniably and profoundly great.

CHAPTER 2

Phase I:
Techniques to Energize Success

There are four techniques we use to energize success in The Nurtured Heart Approach:

Technique 1: Active Recognition (Kodak)

Technique 2: Experiential Recognition (Polaroid)

Technique 3: Proactive Recognition (Canon)

Technique 4: Creative Recognition

You will recall that in the previous chapter we suggested that you think of each of these techniques as similar to the processes of a camera – ways of capturing moments in the mind's eye and reflecting them back to the child. Each of the techniques becomes a slightly different way to take a picture in time, a snapshot if you will, of the child being successful. We refer to three of these techniques by a camera name (Kodak, Polaroid and Canon). If using that terminology is helpful to you, do so.

This chapter will describe each of the techniques in detail and offer you some activities to help you begin to feel at ease with each of them. In the end, however, you will discover that each technique is not necessarily used alone. The techniques are most fluidly used in tandem with one another, but they are best learned and practiced separately in the beginning.

ENERGIZING SUCCESS IS ABOUT GIVING ENERGY IN RESPONSE TO POSITIVES RATHER THAN NEGATIVES.

Technique 1: Active Recognition (Kodak Moments)

This technique involves creating successes that would not otherwise exist and having those successes register within the child in an irrefutable way. The latter is especially important for the child who does not yet trust positive statements because he currently experiences himself only as someone who is always getting in trouble. This child might have a previous accumulation of first-hand experiences of failure via remarks *intended* to set limits, such as "cut that out," "quit that," or worse. No matter how well intended, these remarks are always heard with a tinge of criticism and a perceived implication of failure.

Children who are recipients of remarks like these will come to believe that those comments comprise the truth of who they are. When someone says something nice to these children, they will brace against the compliment with an internally defended stance of, "That's not the truth. I'm really not a good kid. I'm always getting in trouble." **So, to get around that defensiveness, it is vitally important to have *irrefutable* ways to make statements that communicate success.**

In The Nurtured Heart Approach, the first technique for getting beyond the defensive radar in an irrefutable way is *Active Recognition.*

Active Recognition: Watch, describe and document what you see out loud – as if for a blind companion.

With this technique, you say *out loud* what you see the child doing, almost as though you were a camera showing a photo of what the child is doing at that moment. *Do this only when you see a positive behavior, never when the child is doing something that is not okay.* Active Recognitions are "photo opportunities" in which *you construct success* by virtue of how you see things. Watch, describe and document **out loud** what you see. Don't look the other way. The comments should not judge or question, just **reflect.** Put a little tone of enjoyment in your voice. Go with the flow. Ordinary moments are windows of opportunity. Notice both actions and emotions of the child. In essence, you are saying to the child: "Here you are being successful." This is irrefutable evidence to the child that he is *seen* and *held in esteem*. This gets beyond the child's defenses. Be highly specific and not vague. Just notice and say what you see.

An example of how NOT to do this is the typical adult response to a child's drawing. Usually it is a variation of "What a beautiful picture," or "I love your artwork." Instead, Active Recognition recommends that you simply describe what is actually in the picture (such as the actual colors and shapes the child has used) or what you see taking place (such as the process the child is using).

For example, "I see you've made some red circles and green triangles and some of them overlap. And I notice you put quite a few staples along the edge of the page." This comment or remark to the child contains *no judgment or technical critique – nothing that can be perceived as criticism.* In this way, the child knows that she has been seen and acknowledged. The detail makes it irrefutable.

To a child playing a computer game, you might comment, "I see that you are really focused on your game and you somehow managed to move your player through that maze. You seem totally tuned in."

Or, to a child who is playing with multi-colored tiles: "I notice that you have separated the tiles into piles based on color and it looks as if you are starting to build something by alternating colors."

Notice that in these comments there is no judgment or criticism, merely acknowledgement.

Active Recognition: Additional Examples

Rather than saying "What a pretty picture," **INSTEAD** say: "I see you used four different colors, colored the squares green, and used red for a border."

Rather than saying "Thank you," **INSTEAD** say: "You put your shoes and your coat in the closet and closed the door."

Rather than saying "Good job," **INSTEAD** say: "I notice that you are frustrated with your homework, but I see you continuing to work and taking one problem at a time."

Remember: Watch, describe and document exactly what you see, as if for a blind companion.

"Let Sleeping Dogs Lie"

Typically, parents <u>avoid</u> a challenging child when the challenges aren't happening. For example, imagine walking by your child's room en route to your own. You are in the process of completing a project but you notice your child has been playing independently for quite some time. You might be inclined **not** to say 'hello' for two essential reasons – you need to get back to what you were doing and you don't want to get inveigled and accidentally trip the circuits, stirring up some problem behaviors. **Next time, instead of walking (or tiptoeing) by, make face-to-face contact, provide active recognition (see examples above), and then depart.**

Try this.

The next time your child is playing independently or completing a task without prompts, take 10 seconds to give active recognition and then just say 'see you later' and go back to what you were doing.

Process what happened after you complete the above exercise. How did your child respond? Did it motivate him to misbehave or did it motivate him to work harder on his project? You can write down your observations and thoughts below.

_____

_____

_____

_____

_____

Common pitfalls...

• Beware of the trap of waiting to "catch" success. You can "create" ordinary moments of success with this technique. (For example, you might say, "I see you are concentrating fully on your project and trying to get it just right.")

• Avoid energizing negative behaviors. Remember to use this technique when things are going well.

• Avoid judgments or questions. Focus on making clear, concise statements that merely document the child's actions.

Practice this Active Recognition technique several times each day. Challenge yourself to be tuned into the moment. Try to notice as many ways to recognize the actions of others as you can. This is a great technique to practice in just about any setting – home, work or in the community. The more you do it, the more comfortable you will feel, and the more you will notice the positive reactions of those around you!

Active Recognitions appreciate the child for who he really is.

With these kinds of comments, the child feels *in his bones* that he is being held in esteem and that he is worthy of someone's time simply for what he likes to do. He does not have to be doing something spectacular such as hitting a home run at a Little League game. These recognitions allow a parent or teacher to help a child feel loved and cherished *just the way he is right now.* In a nutshell, you capture ordinary moments and reflect them back to the child in a way that he feels cherished.

Active Recognitions allow for creation of honest successes.

Active Recognitions also allow the adult to avoid the trap of waiting to "catch" successes, but rather to "create" successes via ordinary moments. *Active Recognition, then, is simply capturing an ordinary moment and taking a picture of it.* Perhaps real self-esteem is an accumulation of moments such as these where the child essentially feels held in esteem. And perhaps real self-worth is tied to the child's perception that he is worthy of the interest of others, not just for the high-water marks of accomplishment, but for the everyday events in his life. *Demonstrating* esteem and worthiness of time and relationship is infinitely more powerful than merely *telling* a child that he should have self-worth and self-esteem.

Demonstrating esteem and worthiness of time and relationship is infinitely more powerful than merely *telling* a child that he should have self-worth and self-esteem.

Active Recognitions can be used to address emotions and feelings.

Active Recognition is also a great tool for talking about emotions. In our culture, most of us have been taught that certain emotional states are either not acceptable or need to be kept to one's self. To children we often say, Stop acting so angry – no one did anything to you!" or even, "Why are you feeling that way?" We act as if the feeling is something that is not okay and needs to disappear. In contrast, use Active Recognition to acknowledge the child's feeling or emotion without casting judgment.

In actuality, emotional health is not about *not having feelings*; rather, it is about *being in touch with feelings* and being strong enough on the inside to feel and respond to whatever is going on. When we as adults are out of touch with or suppressing our feelings, we either try to escape the discomfort (possibly through addictive behaviors) or subconsciously take it out on someone else. People who are out of touch are all too often frightened of their feelings and are prone to depressed emotions and a depressed lifestyle.

When a person is **in touch** with feelings, he navigates the world with greater ease. He is not afraid of difficult discussions and can use his emotions to gather information and ask for what he wants and needs.

Therefore, use Active Recognition when you see that your child is emotional about something. Don't wait until the emotion passes or becomes a problem to the point where a rule is broken. Go one step beyond by *making that emotional moment into a success*.

For example, "I see that you are upset that I said you couldn't play with your friend right now. I love that you are allowing yourself to feel your feelings and are not taking your anger out on anybody." In essence you are saying to the child that he is being successful for handling his strong feelings well, which will expand his ability to see himself as someone who can do that. It becomes a **first-hand experience** of "It's not a question of whether I can or can't – I *am* handling my strong feelings well."

> When giving Active Recognitions, you might use phrases similar to *"I notice"* and *"I see."* Use Active Recognitions liberally. Be honest! Say *exactly* what you see and notice.

Try this!

For this exercise you will need a partner and puzzle. Take turns practicing Active Recognitions as one of you works the puzzle. For example, "I notice you looked carefully at the colors so that you could find the piece that matched." Or, "I see how organized you are when you are working." Focus on staying in the moment. Notice how you feel as the **recipient.** It feels nice, doesn't it? Notice also how you feel when *giving* Active Recognitions. If you feel uncertain or unsure, that is merely because this is a new and different experience. Applaud yourself for all your hard work so far and keep practicing Active Recognitions again and again. You will be amazed how easily it comes to you. Over time, this will become more automatic.

It may be helpful to break it down into some smaller pieces so that you will easily be able to identify the process of interaction. Take a moment to recall recent interactions with your child.

What you Saw or Noticed	What you Said	Child's Response

Active Recognition Statements

Below is a list of Active Recognition examples. You can use this list to familiarize yourself with the type of remarks that provide irrefutable evidence of success and that promote true self-esteem. Use Active Recognitions liberally. Above all, be honest!

Remember:

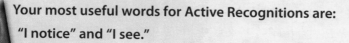

Your most useful words for Active Recognitions are: "I notice" and "I see."

- Sadie, I've noticed the extra effort you've been using while cleaning off the counter.

- Zach annoyed you and I see that you walked away without starting anything.

- I noticed the effort you put into putting your things away in an organized manner.

- I see that you are putting all the colored blocks together to make a pattern.

- I see that you are playing with the dolls pretending that you are the mother.

- I noticed that you got started on your job right away and you are very focused.

- I see you are frustrated with the toy but you are sticking with it to make it work.

- I see that you are upset and I appreciate that you're handling your strong feelings well.

Stay in the **here and now** when giving Active Recognitions. Radiate energy when doing this. Do not lecture, preach, try to make a point or ask a question. **Make every effort to give the child Active Recognitions for at least a few minutes each day.**

Despite your being savvy and persistent, however, you may find that your child perceives Active Recognitions as criticism and shuts down. In this case, without overstating or interpreting, simply document out loud your child's emotional status. Modulate the tone of your voice to fit the situation. For example: "It looks as though your feelings are hurt by…." "It seems like you feel disappointed about…." "I see that you are frustrated with…, but you are…." Having his feelings acknowledged without judgment might open up the opportunity for the child to give you the correct information and also be willing to discuss the situation further. ***Being noticed and recognized, at no matter how basic a level, is powerful acknowledgement and exquisite emotional food.***

Do not get thrown by a child's resistive reactions. Come back in a short while and do more of the same.

Remembering Shamu

Remember the story of Shamu? Keep the spirit of that story in mind as you master these techniques.

The key to Shamu's success was that the trainers started with the rope under water, at the bottom of the tank. Shamu's success occurred slowly, over time. Early on he was rewarded for merely swimming across the rope that was lying at the bottom of the tank. When he made the connection between swimming over the rope and receiving rewards, one day, right on signal, he was able to jump 22 feet into the air to obtain the reward.

This mindset creates opportunities that would not otherwise exist. Once the child finally understands the link between the internal feeling of success and your response in terms of the energy and the emotional reaction you have to give, she will begin to integrate success into every aspect of her life.

How's this going to work with your youngster?

Most younger children soak up comments like this like a sponge and give you clear visual feedback that you had positive influence. Some younger children, however, are uncomfortable with positive statements and will act out as the statement occurs. Some parents and teachers may interpret this as a sign that the approach isn't working and is actually backfiring. Our clinical experience, however, demonstrates that the opposite is true.

The child actually likes the acknowledgment and recognition, but he doesn't yet trust that he can keep you engaged in this manner. Out of fear, he is drawn toward doing what he absolutely knows from past experience – he will attempt to keep you engaged through negativity.

It is crucial that you not fall into the trap of responding with energy and relationship to the negativity. Purposely stand your ground and do this technique with even more resolve. In doing so, you move the child to greater levels of trusting that he, indeed, can believe you notice his goodness.

How's this going to work with teens?

We are certain there are people reading this book who are thinking: "Yeah, right! I'm going to do this with my teenager and she's going to look at me like I'm from another planet and say something like 'Why are you saying all these weird things to me? What'd you do? Read another stupid parenting book or something? Stop saying those silly things to me!'"

Now if you are **NOT** taking a stand, you might then and there run for the hills and abandon the approach. However, if you **ARE** taking a stand, we recommend you dig in and continue doing these Active Recognitions with even more determination.

Creative ways to say it

To a snickering teen you might try, "I hear that you noticed a difference. Thanks for noticing. It feels odd to me, too."

Or: "I did read another parenting book. I felt as if what we were doing just wasn't working. Thanks for being open to my trying something new."

Or: "You're right, I am being different. I realized that I mostly notice all the things that I think you do wrong. Now I want to notice a lot of the good things you do. It's only fair. I'm liking it and you'll get used to it, too."

No matter what your child's reaction, the key is the *photographic opportunity*. "Tim, I love that you feel the difference in what I am doing and that you thought enough to let me know. I can tell my comments sound silly to you and I hear you saying that you want them to stop. I appreciate that you are not arguing or yelling." **(You are still just noticing what you see and hear.)**

You can tell the truth at that point: "I actually did read another parenting book, and I realized that I tend to notice you more when things are going wrong. But, I'm determined to notice as many good things as I can. I apologize that it feels silly – it feels silly to me as well." **(You are still, in essence, proclaiming that stopping is not an option.)**

Or you can be silly and say something such as: "I don't know what's gotten into me. I had a dream and saw myself saying these remarks to you and, in a weird way, it kind of made sense to notice you in this way." **(Again, you are essentially proclaiming that this is now the way it's going to be.)**

When working with "gang" kids, who most often have their "game face" on, you don't have the luxury of seeing the direct impact of these statements. The child is guarded. What works with this approach is actually "trusting" that we are having an impact even though we don't see it. This translates to turning up the dial and actually doing *more* Active Recognitions, with *more* detail and *more* aliveness in the tone and description.

Active Recognition In Action

Co-author Lisa Bravo recently worked with a father who had a difficult 15-year-old son. Here is a poignant story she remembers:

The father contacted me after reading Transforming the Difficult Child: The Nurtured Heart Approach and applying some of the techniques. He said that after several weeks of doing Active Recognitions, he found his son less aggressive, less apt to lash out and more communicative. The father asked me to come and observe their interaction to make sure they were on track.

When I met Joshua, he was less than enthusiastic about my being in his home. Although his body language told me he wanted nothing to do with this "therapy stuff," he still tried to be respectful and speak to me. (This is where I started the rope!)

I asked Joshua, if he could pick three things to change about the way he is parented, what would they be? He said that he was annoyed with his Dad's noticing "everything" that he did. He went on to say that he thought it was stupid that his father was being so nice. He looked at me and asked, "Why is he noticing everything good about me?" While delivering his gripes about his father's new way of seeing him, his body language was open, he had a smile on his face, and he was making eye contact. This told me that he was, on some level, completely internalizing his father's new way of relating. Although he felt the need to test this new awareness by his father, it was clear that he noticed a huge change in the way they were all interacting.

Technique 2: Experiential Recognition (Polaroid Moments)

Experiential Recognition is an extension of Active Recognition with a new twist – that of instilling values. We have so many values in our hearts that we want to impart to our kids. Among others, we want them to be responsible, respectful and cooperative. We would like them to be thoughtful, kind and considerate. We expect them to exhibit a good attitude, good manners and good judgment.

Unfortunately, however, we tend to try to teach values when children are the least receptive; that is, when they have done something wrong or something that does not adhere to the values we as adults wish them to live by. For example, we might find ourselves saying, "Why would you take that toy from your friend while she's playing with it? That's not very considerate!" Or, "Stop eating your food with your fingers. Mind your manners. Haven't I raised you better than that?" There is an endless variety of other such statements.

Although these statements are well-meaning attempts to appeal to our children's sense of right and wrong and to sway them to the "right" way of thinking, they unintentionally energize negative behavior instead of success. Why? It is because of our expenditure of emotion, time, conversation and relationship that occurs at those times.

But the good news is we can help our kids recognize when their *natural behaviors* reflect the values we wish them to hold. By recognizing them when these values are occurring naturally, we energize positive behaviors and take a step toward building that positive portfolio that leads to inner wealth and transformation.

EXPERIENTIAL RECOGNITIONS: An opportunity to appreciate the qualities that you want to see grow.

This is a technique to teach values and to highlight the healthy qualities you wish to enhance in your child. Children often do not know how to evaluate their experiences, and they need our help. We typically choose to teach the qualities and life skills that we value at the *very worst times*, so that we accidentally energize the opposite of what we want.

This technique energizes the child at the moment he is demonstrating even small amounts of the qualities you want to see develop.

THINK SHAMU – THINK TOLLBOOTH ATTENDANT

STEAL THE MOMENT

The truth is that, when the child is NOT breaking the rules, she IS being successful, she IS being respectful, she IS cooperating, she IS being responsible, she IS using good judgment and she IS being thoughtful. With the right techniques, we can easily reflect successes back to the child AS THEY ARE OCCURRING!

When you notice a child is exhibiting a behavior that you want him to incorporate into his life, rather than ignoring it, verbally document the desired behavior with your recognition and appreciation. Make a big deal about the good stuff. Use **value** words: "That shows **respect**," "That shows **good judgment**," "That shows a lot of **thoughtfulness**," "That shows **responsibility**," "That shows excellent **cooperation**." The secrets to making this work are:
1. Radiating lots of energy as you make your positive statements; and
2. Elaborating as much as possible – giving rich details about what you see and why you appreciate it.

Below are examples of Experiential Recognition statements. You can use this list to further familiarize yourself with the technique as well as to practice giving Experiential Recognitions.

Some useful phrases for Experiential Recognitions are **"I appreciate," "I love," "I like,"** and **"I'm pleased."** Use Experiential Recognitions liberally. Above all, be honest!

- I appreciate the *good choice* you made to speak *thoughtfully*.

- I love that you've shown *responsibility* in putting away the blocks.

- I appreciate that you just *took "no" for an answer* without arguing or fussing. Thanks for being so *respectful*.

- I'm very pleased that you've been doing your chores *without being told*. You are being *very considerate* and that's a great quality.

Experiential Recognition Examples – Continued

- I appreciate that you've been *sharing* with your friend. That's a *great attitude.*

- I like it when you are *focused* on your project. That shows *thoughtfulness.*

- I love it that you cleaned your place *without being asked.* That shows *responsibility.*

- I like how *nice* you were to Kayla when she felt sad. That really shows *compassion.*

- You *did what I asked* right away. You *followed directions* beautifully.

- You've been much *kinder* with your friends. I really appreciate the *cooperation* you've been using.

- I'm pleased that you were *honest* when it would have been easy to lie. That shows *integrity.*

- You've been using much more *self-control* when you're mad. I appreciate that very much.

What are the values and qualities you would like your child to incorporate into his life or that you want to see enhanced? You can make a written list or a mental list. Below are lines where you can write down those qualities. Go beyond that and also describe a recent interaction between the two of you when one of those qualities was exhibited but you neglected to recognize it.

_____

_____

_____

_____

_____

Again, stay in the here and now when giving Experiential Recognitions. Radiate energy. Do not lecture, preach, try to make a point or debate. Make every effort to see that the child is the recipient of Active *and* Experiential Recognitions for at least five minutes each day.

Experiment	
Spend an entire day counting how many times you complimented your child's success. Tally up your statements for each hour and then for the day.	How much is enough? How much is too much? (See below and let's talk numbers…)

Can you spare 300 seconds (just 5 minutes) a day to create transformation?

You do the math…

- 300 divided by 10 = 30
  (10 recognitions that take 30 seconds each = 5 minutes)

- 300 divided by 15 = 20
  (15 recognitions that take 20 seconds each = 5 minutes)

- 300 divided by 20 = 15
  (20 recognitions that take 15 seconds each = 5 minutes)

This is what you are aiming for. However you choose to divide it is up to you. Approach your child 30 times a day for 10 seconds each and create very short but powerful statements of success. Let your heart *sing appreciation.*

...an apple a day...

If you are reading this page, you have completed several exercises and are well on your way to transforming your child. Congratulations!

Technique 3: Proactive Recognition (Canon Moments)

Proactive Recognition is yet another opportunity to take Active Recognition a step further. When do we normally choose to teach rules? The answer is: when a rule is being broken. But this gives the payoff of energy at the worst possible time, and it makes matters worse for children with patterns of negativity. Proactive Recognitions, on the other hand, are opportunities to notice the child **when he is not breaking rules.** This is another way of taking a moment, freezing it, and describing it to the child as a success. The trick here is to specifically describe the moment in a manner that is irrefutable. In Proactive Recognition, the adult refers to the rules and celebrates the child when he is **not breaking them.**

For example, you pass by the family room and your son is sitting quietly watching television with his sister. A Proactive Recognition at that time might be something like, "I appreciate that you are not teasing or bothering your sister or calling her names. Thank you very much for being considerate. That's a great choice to be kind to her."

In Proactive Recognition, you are noticing when things are **going right** and when **rules are not being broken** … and you **energize** these situations by commenting on them **at that time.**

Keep in mind that you must always exert effort when rules are NOT being broken. When a child is proactively recognized when he is NOT breaking a rule, he realizes that he is being appreciated (<u>and</u> given energy) when he is following the rules instead of when he isn't. **This gives recognition to self-control and healthy power.**

So why not just walk on by?

You may be wondering what the harm is in simply letting the good stuff happen and not paying a lot of attention to it. Remember, in keeping with the "Shamu-Tollbooth Attendant" philosophy, we must CREATE successes that might not otherwise exist. While it is tempting to revel in the momentary peace and quiet, it does little to alter the portfolio you have been working so hard to change. Doing something different in these moments changes the flow of energy and gets things moving in the right direction. So, go ahead and make a fuss when things are going well!

Proactive Recognitions clarify the limits and set the stage for rules and consequences to really have an effect.

With Proactive Recognitions, the child also sees that Mom or Dad really knows the rules cold. There is no wiggle room. The boundaries between right and wrong become redefined at a higher level of clarity so that the child knows all the more clearly when he steps out of bounds.

In effect, by making these kinds of statements throughout the day, the child comes to know that **you know the rules** and that you know **he knows the rules.** Like the out-of-bounds line in a video game or in sports, the rules become more and more clear. This helps enormously when the consequences phase of The Nurtured Heart Approach is introduced to the child. (Hold your questions about rules and consequences and we will discuss more about them later. For right now, familiarize yourself with Proactive Recognitions and how to give them.)

Proactive Recognition

We often give the payoff of our energy at the worst possible time: when the rule has already been broken! Our energy then becomes a reward. This makes matters worse for children with existing patterns of negativity.

Again, this is like accidentally handing the child a $100 bill for having made a choice to break a rule. Nobody would dream of doing this on purpose. Instead, use *Proactive Recognition*.

- Energize and show appreciation of the child when the rules are NOT being broken.

- Give recognition to self-control and healthy power.

- There is *always* an underlying effort when rules are NOT being broken.

- Proactive Recognitions clarify the limits and set the stage for rules and consequences to really have an effect.

Examples of Proactive Recognitions

I like…I love…I appreciate…I am impressed…I am proud…I am pleased…Thanks for…

Proactive Recognitions are used to acknowledge when a child has NOT broken a rule. Consider using the words above to deliver Proactive Recognitions. Use Proactive Recognitions liberally. Above all, be honest!

So, what does Proactive Recognition sound like?

- "I like it when you *didn't hit back* and you *managed your feelings*."

- "I like it that you are *not being destructive* and *not being aggressive*."

Proactive Recognition – Continued

- "I appreciate that you have *not been rude* to your teachers. Thank you for choosing good manners."

- "I'm impressed that you *didn't complain about your bedtime* tonight. You readied yourself and went right to bed *without arguing*. That is a powerful way to show peacefulness."

- "Thanks for *getting back in control of strong feelings*. You were really mad and you calmed yourself down without any help. Good job for showing excellent self-control."

- "Even though you didn't want to, you *followed directions* and got in line when the teacher asked you to. You are very powerful when you do that."

- "You *didn't let phone calls interfere with doing your homework*. That shows good judgment and I am so pleased about that."

- "You *have not been screaming or yelling* since your time-out. I really appreciate the extra self-control you're using…especially since I can see that you are still disappointed."

- "I appreciate that you *haven't been demanding*. Good job for being thoughtful."

THERE ARE COUNTLESS OPPORTUNITIES DURING THE DAY TO NOTICE WHEN A CHILD IS **NOT BREAKING A RULE.**

 If you're in the habit of scolding or fussing about your child's bad behaviors, replace giving energy to adversity by making a fuss over the good stuff…for RULES NOT BEING BROKEN.

Experiment With Making A Big Deal When Things Are Going Well (Not Going Wrong)

In the moments when the rules are NOT being broken, take the opportunity to create success by providing specific appreciation. Notice how your child responds in this moment and how this changes your connections with your child. Take a moment to jot down your observations:

_____

_____

_____

_____

_____

Remember to stay in the here and now when giving Proactive Recognitions. Even if the child has recently broken a rule, but rules are not being broken this very second, that's an immediate opportunity for a Proactive Recognition. The truth of the moment is that the child is RIGHT NOW making a good choice. Radiate energy when doing this.

Make every effort to continue to see that the child is the recipient of Active Recognitions, Experiential Recognitions and Proactive Recognitions for at least five minutes each day. Combine the techniques to suit your style and the situation.

Finally, when giving Active, Experiential and Proactive Recognitions, DO NOT BE AFRAID TO USE THE "BIG WORDS" (e.g., integrity, character, compassion, self-control, responsibility, attitude.) These words are honest, they teach the child what the words really mean, and they make the boundaries very clear to the child. Ultimately they are character building. We have actually experimented extensively with using these words with young children, and they seem to absorb the meaning and intent perfectly, especially when the word is used in the context of a described situation.

Big Words List

Using "significant" words takes communication with your child to another level. It conveys the message that she is worth more thoughtful and powerful words. Even if your child does not have an expansive vocabulary, she will surely respond to your "Big Words" praise. Here are some examples:

- "I love the way you are choosing to be *cooperative*."

- "You are showing you have a lot of *integrity* right now."

- "I like the way you are being *considerate* right now."

- "I really appreciate how you are planning ahead. That shows you are *responsible*."

- "That was a *creative* answer. You are really thinking outside the box."

- "Your taking turns shows me you are being a *peacemaker*."

- "You are being successful in being a *problem solver*."

- "Right now you are being very *insightful*."

- "You keep trying even though you are frustrated. You are showing great *determination*."

- "You are being very *wise* right now."

- "Your action shows that you have a *tender heart*."

- "You are demonstrating great *analytic skills* in solving the problem."

- "Right now you are showing *respect* both for yourself and others."

- "Right now you are demonstrating *magnificent thinking*."

- "I trust you to rely on your *wisdom* to solve the problem."

Technique 4: Creative Recognition

Improving our Children's Response to our Requests

As parents or teachers, we generally make requests of our children that inadvertently advertise options and imply a choice. We frequently use requests that begin with "would you…?" "could you…?" or "please…." The problem is that children with existing patterns of negativity will often make a choice based on where they can find the bigger payoff of energy. Given an option, they will choose not to follow a request because their past experience indicates that choice will net more intense relationship and energy. Typically, this manifests itself in lack of cooperation or in oppositional behavior. Creative Recognition eliminates these options and serves to clarify expectations and to avoid confusion on the child's part.

In our society, we value etiquette. Having good manners, being polite, and waiting your turn are all part of the social code. We are taught that part of being a good parent is instilling these values in our children. Some of the very first words children learn are "please" and "thank you."

The suggestion that we not "ask" our children to do chores, complete given tasks, etc., is a difficult one for parents and teachers because of our value system. Consider that it is possible to state clearly and concisely what we "need" the child to do while still being respectful and nurturing. **How** we make requests of the child makes all the difference.

Avoiding ambiguous requests and instead using requests that begin with "I need you to…" or "I want you to…" eliminates the options, avoids the confusion and sets the stage for success. For example, "Would you please wipe the table?" is a request that accidentally implies a choice. A request that sets the stage for success, such as "I need you to wipe the table," is clearer and reduces the chance that the child will respond out of his negativity.

When the child has followed the request, always recognize and appreciate any movement in the desired direction. Make the requests as simple as they need to be to create at least a few successes each day. Make a big deal when the child does what you ask.

Remember to reinforce and energize the child's efforts and response to your request. For example, "I notice that you picked up nearly all the blocks off the floor and put them on the shelves in order. I really appreciate how well you listened and how you are doing what I asked. Now I need you to get the last three blocks from the floor and put them away, too." **Always remember to reinforce honestly.**

Making clearer requests is not a guarantee, but they make it far more likely that the child will comply.

The MORE INTENSE the child,
the MORE INTENSE the intervention.

You must make your approach more powerful for the more difficult child.

In the story of David earlier in this chapter, David's father understood that in order to begin to create successes for his exceedingly oppositional son, he needed to begin with the rope at the bottom of the tank. He began creating successes by making a VERY BIG DEAL out of a normal, every-day experience of closing the car door. When David was already in the act of closing the door, his father said, "David, *I need you to* close the door." No matter how oppositional the child, the deed was already in progress and it was too late for David himself to reverse it. So, when the door clicked closed, his father said, "David, thanks for listening so well and thanks for doing exactly what I asked. That's great that you followed the direction."

Then, just as David started to fasten his seat belt, his dad turned to him and told him "*I need you to* put your seat belt on." Again, it was a done deal. The father then very creatively accused David of being successful: "Thank you for doing just what I asked you to do, David. This time it was as if you heard my request inside your brain before I even said it. You knew what I wanted and you cooperated. I appreciate that."

The techniques are meant to work "in the moment."

An important point to remember with all of the techniques is that they are meant to work in the moment. Telling the truth of the moment and leaving the past and future out of it brings a sense of honesty and a spiritual presence to any situation. The child might have argued three minutes ago and might be about to argue again, but *right now she isn't*! When one is purely in the moment, the truth is blatantly evident. We don't need postured successes to appreciate, but rather the utter simplicity of human moments.

David's father began with the rope at the bottom of the pool, creating success where it otherwise did not exist. Making the choice to recognize an everyday moment as having potential for success, he seized that opportunity and immediately and vigorously energized the success. Following these exceedingly simple recognitions by his father to get the process going, David began to do the unimaginable. He began to respond positively to increasingly complicated requests such as "You need to go clean your room." Those acts and the many like it that followed began David toward a path of building a positive portfolio and ultimately led to inner wealth and transformation in David's heart.

The point is that very, very difficult children, such as David, require that we use the techniques more often, with more specificity and detail, and with more vigor in our responses by way of greater animation and emotion. Energize this moment and the next moment and the next. Reflect back to your child her greatness that she might not otherwise see. Shine the dazzling light of success back into her eyes and, as a result, her light will shine brighter and greater.

Staying in the moment is the pivotal piece.

Until the consequence phase is in place, give as little energy to negativity as possible. If a rule is broken, simply state: "That's a broken rule…that's a time-out." Keep it unceremonious and do not worry if the child does not complete the time-out. If the time-out gets done well, energize the success with appreciation. Make a BIG FUSS over the good stuff and avoid giving any recognition to negativity. **Radiate energy and weave success into any possible endeavor.** Use comments that play both ends of the opportunity: what *is* happening that can be held up as a success and what *isn't* happening that can be held up as a success.

To help you learn and practice the technique, below are examples of Creative Recognition as it might occur in an everyday sequence or application.

Examples of Creative Recognition

"I need you to pick up your toys right now." Then say something such as:
> "I see you picking up toys off the floor."
> "I like it when you do what I ask."
> "Thanks for clearing the floor on time."

"I need you to wipe off the counter." Then say:
"Thanks for using a clean cloth."
"I can really see the effort you are making."
"I appreciate your help in the kitchen."

If the acknowledgements and recognition are not detailed and specific, the child's defensive radar comes into play. It absolutely has to be made clear what specific actions were valued. Merely saying "thank you" and "good job" to the child doesn't convey to the child that she has truly and deeply been seen and appreciated.

Creative Recognitions Practice Scenario

Your child comes into the room and asks if she can go out to play. You notice that she has not put away the Legos® she had been playing with, nor has she cleaned up from the snack she had been eating. Using the example above, take a moment to write down the new dialogue you might have with your child. Be sure to use the techniques we have just discussed.

_____

_____

_____

_____

_____

_____

_____

_____

_____

_____

_____

_____

_____

_____

_____

CHECK YOURSELF!

For your consideration, here are a few examples of phrases we might have used in the previous exercise:

"I see that you asked for permission (to go out and play)." (Active Recognition – Kodaks)

"I notice that you are picking up all of the pieces." (Active Recognition – Kodaks)

"I like that you asked for permission – that shows me you are very responsible." (Experiential Recognition – Polaroids)

"I appreciate that you are cleaning up your Legos® and your snack without making a fuss. That is having a great attitude AND being responsible!" (Experiential Recognition – Polaroids)

"I appreciate that you and your sister are cleaning up your toys without arguing or complaining. That shows a lot of cooperation." (Proactive Recognition – Canons)

"Even though you are frustrated that you have to clean up your space, you are really holding it together. You are not complaining or crying. Right now you are being responsible and mature." (Proactive Recognition – Canons)

"I need you to pick up your Legos® and snack, and then you may go outside. I see that you are disappointed but you are handling it well by doing what I have asked and still having such a great attitude. Right now you are being very responsible." (Creative Recognition – Canons)

Creative Recognition: Prescription

- Use simple and clear requests to create five to ten "successes" daily. Encourage the child by making requests that are very doable and that the child might predictably perform without a struggle; then, as time passes, gradually make bigger requests.

- Use your parenting creativity through requests that invite compliance and applause rather than conventional requests that are less clear ("Put your dirty clothes in the hamper every morning" rather than "Please do your chores.") Consciously practice and use command-type requests versus question-type requests that invite negative responses from the child ("I need you to…" rather than "Could you please…?").

- Recognize and appreciate even the small efforts your child makes. Be specific with examples of behavior you observe. Advance your level of awareness and appreciation to include the following:
  - Efforts made by the child that show movement in the right direction
  - Evidence that the child is displaying a good attitude
  - Any time the child makes a smart choice – even a little one

Creative Recognitions – More Practice

Reframe these sentences so that they are more concise and clear.

1. Please put your things away.

   _____

2. Are you going to get ready for bed?

   _____

3. Do you want to help me fold the clothes?

   _____

4. Will you bring in the groceries?

   _____

5. Would you please set the table?

_____

6. Please go to bed.

_____

Here are some possible ways to restate the above requests using Creative Recognition.

1. I need you to put your things away.

2. It's time now to get ready for bed.

3. I need you to help me fold the clothes.

4. I need you to help me bring in the groceries.

5. I want you to set the table now.

6. Right now, it's time to go to bed.

Remember: KEEP IT SHORT, SIMPLE, AND DIRECT, especially with the oppositional child. Follow up the child's compliance with specific recognition of her success.

Remain firm and remember your Stands: "I'm not going to let my child pull me into a pattern of failure and payoffs for negativity. I'm going to do what it takes to pull my child in the direction of success."

This mantra is the focus of Creative Recognition. Write it down and place it in a place where you will see it several times a day. Say it aloud when you see it. Say it silently in your thoughts when you notice your child's difficult behavior beginning to emerge. This affirmation represents your resolve to change your child's situation. It is a very powerful stance and will anchor you for future strategies involving rules, boundaries and consequences.

Parents and teachers make the most powerful therapists.
Whether or not we see ourselves in that role, we indeed have a **therapeutic** impact. The root of that word simply means **agent of change.**

Parents and teachers have so much potential impact because they have more time with the child, and within that time, they have much more context, meaning and relationship.

APPLAUSE! APPLAUSE!

If you've come this far, you deserve applause for your efforts, creativity and power!

The Wrap Up

Now you are familiar with and have practiced the techniques of The Nurtured Heart Approach. Here's a summary of the important concepts you have learned.

- Active Recognition acknowledges children in an irrefutable way by commenting out loud to them in a nonjudgmental manner simply what they are doing or feeling, as if taking a picture in time.

- We know that we can instill values in our children by using Experiential Recognition – a new twist on Active Recognition – that involves adding value words to our remarks.

- We are alert to instances when the child is NOT breaking a rule and we energize those times by use of Proactive Recognition.

- By eliminating options from our requests to the child, we can be clearer and set the stage for success. This is Creative Recognition.

The Wrap Up – Continued

- Some children might require more intervention. With these children, we do the techniques more frequently, we make the recognition and appreciation more specific and detailed, and we give more of our animation and emotion to the comments.

- We need always to "stay in the moment" and make a big fuss over what is happening *right now* that can be held up as successful, forgetting the past and not concerned with the future.

- Finally, we recognize that, for the time being, while we are learning how to use the techniques to create success, we simply and unceremoniously inform the child that a rule has been broken and give him a quick time-out. If the time-out is done well, we energize that success. If the time-out is not done well, we wait for the next opportunity to begin to energize success.

The Next Step

You have come a long way toward understanding The Nurtured Heart Approach. Bravo and congratulations! Take whatever time you need to learn and then to begin to apply the techniques and to feel comfortable with them. Forgive yourself when you make an error, give yourself a break, and then begin the techniques again at the very first opportunity. Stay the course! Continue the techniques and do not become discouraged! The Nurtured Heart Approach works!

Your child might have responded to The Nurtured Heart Approach so well that you might believe you do not need to proceed. Even if things are now going great, however, we highly recommend the next crucial step.

You are now ready to proceed to the next phase: consequences, limit setting and the all-important third Stand.

CHAPTER 3

Phase II:
Consequences and Limit Setting

The Creative Recognition techniques previously discussed work beautifully to "hijack" children into success, but they are not the only techniques to master. Depending upon just how intense the child has been in the past and how long an undesirable behavior pattern has existed, you may find at this juncture that you are only partway to your goals. The negative habits may still seem to have a life of their own. If you have Stands 1 and 2 in motion – **Energizing Success** and **Refusing to Energize Negativity** – the time is now perfect to explore the third Stand, **Consequences and Limit Setting:** "Here are the rules and here's what happens when you break a rule."

The Basketball Game

Picture yourself at a basketball game. You are sitting in the stands and you observe the starting players out on the floor and the substitutes on the bench. You also notice that there are a couple of officials in striped shirts. One official blows the whistle and the game begins. While you are watching the game unfold, you also notice that the players on the floor carefully observe the boundary line that encloses the official playing area.

Among other aspects of the game, you note that when a player with the ball touches that boundary line, the referee immediately blows his whistle and unceremoniously notes the infraction. Play stops, and an appropriate consequence is meted out to the offending athlete. You also observe that it seems that the players know the rule, the referee knows the rule, and each knows that the other knows the rule.

In the case of basketball, as well as in other games, that boundary line is perfectly clear and respected both by players and officials. Once a player steps even fractionally on that boundary line, and the referee notices it, he is declared out of bounds, and a consequence occurs. Notice that the referee does not lecture, cajole or incite the player. There's no need for discussion or explanation. It's pure and simple. An infraction is an infraction and it always nets a consequence. No arguing, no warnings, no tantrums on the part of either the player or the official – nothing interferes with delivery of the consequence. After the consequence is served, the offender is right back in the game and it continues with all its vitality and energy.

And so it is with consequences and limit setting in The Nurtured Heart Approach. But first, let's take a few minutes to think in a general way about rules, boundaries, limits and consequences.

In basketball, the rules are perfectly clear and both the players and officials know them.

There has been a movement in education in the past few years to use only "positive rules" with children. Such rules are stated in the affirmative, such as "Be respectful," "Use good manners" and "Act responsibly." Here's the problem: What is the *defining line* in a positive rule that allows the referee to say, "Oops, your foot was on the line?" Positive rules cause the line of demarcation to be too fuzzy. Positive rules make it much harder for challenging children to function because they do not have a clear sense of when they are out of bounds and when they are in, and the same is true for the referee.

How far onto the line does the player have to step before he is whistled? How much disrespect needs to occur before a child officially breaks the rule? How much do the manners have to be violated before they are no longer good manners? To the extent that you cannot detect when the foot is out of bounds, it is that much harder to discern when the player is clearly inbounds. Just imagine a basketball game where the boundary lines are fuzzy, blurry or zigzagged and it becomes open to discussion as to whether the boundary line has been violated. Positive rules essentially blur the line.

How fuzzy are the lines on your court?

Do the rules change depending on your mood?

Rules that start with "no" are clear.

Rules that start with "no" lend themselves to so much more clarity. If you were to ask groups of challenging children what kinds of rules are needed for the group, they invariably reel off a host of rules that are much clearer and more structured than conventional positive rules. They will say rules such as "No bad words," "No hitting," "No name calling," "No breaking things," and "No arguing." Rules that start with "no" resonate with much more clarity, particularly for the difficult child. **Remember that our children cannot live their lives with clarity unless we lend them clarity.**

Because we are already providing recognition of success for rules not being broken, rules that start with "no" help provide structure for both the parent and the child.

And, about 99% of the time you can be sure that a child knows exactly when he breaks a rule. It then becomes totally unnecessary to tell the child he broke a rule or which one, and doing so actually winds up focusing on the negative, i.e., giving out $100 bills. As in basketball, the situation simply calls for an unceremonious notification that a consequence is called for. Any discussion, explanations or warnings at that point are not only disadvantageous, but they contradict the new direction we are taking. It reinforces the child's impression that he gets more out of life through adversity (an impression we hope is nearly extinct by now through your diligent efforts).

What, I don't need to post the rules anymore?

That's right! If you apply the techniques discussed in previous chapters AND enforce clear boundaries and expectations, you will no longer have to argue about the rules. PROMISE!

Clear boundaries set up more opportunities for creating success.

"No" rules not only set the limit and allow for clear enforcement, but they also open up infinite opportunities for applause and success. After the child serves the consequence for a broken rule, the door is wide open for you, the parent, to use this as an opportunity to create success. **That is, you can accuse the child of being successful for completing a time-out and for not breaking that very same rule in this new present moment.** You can give energy and juice to the fact that the child accepted her consequence well and served it well. In essence, you are turning a negative into a success and simultaneously providing emotional nourishment.

To Tell the Truth, the Whole Truth, and Nothing But the Truth

Let's say your children have been arguing on three occasions during the day. If each argument takes approximately 15 minutes, that's a total of 45 minutes. If your children are awake for 12 hours, the truth is they have NOT been fighting for 11 hours and 15 minutes. THIS IS A SUCCESS! Keep it in perspective. Congratulate them on the fact that they did not argue for most of the day.

Proceed with Caution!

This is a pitfall for many parents. The child knows she broke a rule. Like in basketball, the slip simply calls for an unceremonious notification. The consequence is given in the moment – it is over and done. Any warning given at this moment contradicts the new direction you have taken. The trick is NOT to let her think she gets MORE – more relationship, more warmth, more intimacy, more connection, more animation – when things are going wrong. We want her to see that she gets so much more when she makes good choices.

In some cases, positive rules are okay, as long as the child CLEARLY knows where the boundary lines are and immediately knows the consequence. Please understand, however, that they are a slippery slope and we strongly recommend the clarity of rules that begin with "no". Children love the clarity. It helps them live their lives with greater lucidity.

In basketball, the referee does not look the other way.

The Consequence Stand reminds us to **refuse to ignore or look the other way** when a consequence is needed. The basketball official does not look the other way, but rather quickly notes the infraction and almost as rapidly doles out the consequence.

The same goes for The Nurtured Heart Approach. As on the basketball court, the parent observes an infraction, immediately announces in an unceremonious manner that a rule has been broken and informs the child, without warning, discussion or explanation, of the consequence. That's an example of a "squeaky clean" consequence. **In essence, looking the other way is a type of warning to the child, and warnings only reinforce the negativity.**

Warnings keep the child off balance.

The other problem with warnings is that they keep the child off balance. For example, when we are having a great day and everything seems rosy, we might let a few minor infractions slide and give some warnings instead of consequences. In contrast, if we are personally having a frustrating day and in a pretty foul mood, we might have less patience with our child and give consequences for those very same infractions. We are keeping the child off balance with our inconsistency.

If you live with a master negotiator, a child who constantly wants to debate and find the loopholes, you may be wondering how in the world you are going to get this to work. Remember, there is nothing wrong with healthy negotiation – except if it happens at the perfectly wrong time. Confused? Think about it: When the dialogue only happens with moments of success, what you will create is MORE of the same. To further illustrate this concept, take a look at the following story.

The Story of Elena

Working with a family comprised of a 4-year-old girl and her parents who had read The Nurtured Heart Approach book but felt they needed more direct feedback about how they were implementing the approach.

With observation, it became clear that this highly explorative little girl needed to know where the line was to a much more precise degree than the typical challenging child needs. She was highly impulsive and had a need to touch everything around her.

Glasser decided to create "on the spot" rules to meet the circumstances of the moment. He would wait until she was NOT touching something and say, "Right now, Elena, you are looking at those things on the table and wondering if there is a rule about whether they can be touched. Even though you want to touch them, you have not. That shows a lot of self-control." Or in another instance, he would say: "Right now you are not interrupting, Elena. You are showing a lot of respect." When she was touching things, he would deliver an unceremonious time-out and moments later, hijack her back into further success. Within the hour, the child was responding to moment, after moment, after moment of successes!

Warnings reinforce negativity and provide relationship at the wrong time.

If our rules are not clear, it becomes habitually easy to give warning after warning as the child pushes the boundary. Warnings are not used in The Nurtured Heart Approach because, unfortunately, they are rewards, particularly for an intense child. When warnings are given, the charge of energy and relationship is still essentially flowing at the *wrong moment in time*. In fact, any explanation is still reinforcement or reward. Saying something like, "Joey, I don't like when you are mean to your brother, now don't do it again," is still evidence of relationship when things are going wrong. So is "Joey, I'll be forced to give you a consequence if…." In essence, you are throwing another log on the very fire that you are attempting to put out. Warnings send a message to the wrong portfolio.

Warnings can easily become a moving target, confusing the child at best and richly rewarding him at worst. It is almost impossible to maintain any kind of consistency when there are warnings. And, although in our society we tend to think of warnings as compassionate, our inconsistencies create an unpredictable world for our child that inadvertently is anything but compassionate. Warnings will NOT get you where you want to go.

Remember: Warnings send a message to the wrong portfolio!

What happens if I blow it?

We are all human, and changing patterns takes practice and consistency. If you fall into old patterns, catch yourself, forgive yourself and get right back on track. When you do this, in actuality, you are modeling healthy power and good choices for your child.

Consequences

Most of our society believes that the power of a consequence lies in how severe, how punitive or how drastic it is. The thinking seems to be that if the punishment is long enough, strong enough or "tough" enough, the child will finally have his awakening and never do the unwanted deed again. In The Nurtured Heart Approach, however, we do not subscribe to this theory. The real power of a consequence lies in simply creating a momentary interruption in the problem that's occurring, and afterward jumping right back to the next available moment of success.

The Nurtured Heart Approach differs from other methods in that consequences are NOT about altering the child's thinking by way of how harsh, drastic or punitive a consequence is; rather, the impact is obtained by **building the child's inner wealth. That's where the awakening really occurs.** Giving positives in the moment is what is powerful.

The REAL power of the consequence is the momentary interruption that gives the child the impression that there has been a result of her action. It opens the door for the REAL awakening that happens through the next series of successes – successes that occur when the problem ISN'T happening.

Eliminate The Warnings!

Take a look at the following scenarios. Notice how the warnings create confusion and feed negativity, making the lines fuzzy:

Scenario 1: You are driving home from a long day of shopping with your two children in the back seat. Your oldest begins to tease his sister, most likely out of boredom. You say:

- "You guys, please stop fighting!" **(Warning)**

- "If you do that again, you will be in trouble!" **(Warning)**

- "Nicholas, how do you think it makes your sister feel when you talk to her that way?" **(Warning)**

By contrast, a "squeaky clean" time-out:

- "Nicholas, that's a time-out." (Nicholas stops talking, sits back, looks out the window.) A few moments later you say, "Nicholas, thanks for putting yourself back in the game. Right now you are being respectful and kind." **(Back to success)**

Scenario 2: Your teenager gets in trouble for cussing at another child at school. When you attempt to calmly discuss it with him, he blows up and begins to speak to you in a disrespectful manner. You say:

- "Jason, please lower your voice!" **(Warning)**

- "Why are you yelling? That's not very nice." **(Warning)**

- "I will give you one more chance. If you do not tell me what happened, I am going to call your teacher." **(Warning)**

By contrast, a "squeaky clean" time-out:

- "That's a time-out" (or "let's take a break" or "that's a reset"). Your child stops ranting. Moments later you make eye contact and say, "Your time-out's over. Thanks for getting back in the game. Even though you are upset, right now you are being respectful and showing a lot of self-control." **(Back to success)**

Isn't this like letting them get away with it?

At first glance, our methods may seem overly permissive. If you have parented with traditional tools up until now, it may seem strange and unnatural not to nag, intervene or correct. The truth is, providing clear structure and boundaries is MORE strict than intermittent punishment and inconsistent warnings.

When your child is doing something wrong, challenge yourself to trust the process of this approach. You may have already experienced profound changes in your relationship with your child. If so, remind yourself how far you have come, and keep up your amazing transformative work. You are changing the life of your child with each and every step.

Like in the video game examples earlier, our goal is to enact a consequence in a way that lets the child know she has made a poor choice at the moment but can soon get back into the game and can avoid another consequence for the same behavior any time she chooses. She completes the consequence and is motivated to move forward. The real and desired movement is a result of the child's growing sense of successfulness. It is not the punishment but the successes that sway the direction of the child's thinking and choices. In fact, the time-out can actually be more of an "illusion" if you treat it creatively, as in the following example:

It's how you connect the dots...

An eight-year-old was fussing and crabby and trying to get her mother's attention in a very demonstrative way. As she flopped herself on the couch with a whining screech, the mother did not feed this negativity and remained silent. Within moments, the girl pulled herself back together, sat up, took a deep breath and in a calm voice, said, "Mommy, can I please have a glass of milk?" Looking at her, the mother said, "Thanks for doing your time-out so well. I am glad to see that you are back on track." The girl stopped for a moment and said, "Hey, I wasn't in time-out…oh, maybe I was."

The point is, even though her mother did not broadcast that her daughter was in time-out, she created the illusion that a time-out had occurred and that the girl had already completed it. In this way, the mother was able to hijack her child into success and celebrate her choice of self-control in a clear and concrete way. By applying the energizing tools of the approach, the energy of the moment was rerouted into a moment of success for both the parent and the child.

All consequences in reality are "time-outs."

Almost all forms of a consequence – removing privileges or adding choices or taking things away – are essentially a time-out. When the child is performing his consequence, his internal experience is always one of 'missing out.' This feels to him like being out of the loop; therefore, this in essence is still a time-out. Also, any type of time-out can be contaminated with rewards, because to the extent we give relationship, words, emotion, connection and energy when things are going wrong, we are rewarding adversity. **In effect it's like saying "here's a consequence and by the way, here's $100."**

Children then become easily confused about what an incentive is and what a real consequence is. They know we don't want them to break another rule, but they remain drawn as if by a magnetic force to the adventure of rule breaking because we demonstrate irrefutably that this is where the juice is. **This is one main reason why conventional time-outs fail to be effective.**

Time-outs are a separation of connection and relationship. Time-ins are a flow of energy and relationship *in connection with a sense of success*. Essentially, if you are adhering to The Nurtured Heart Approach techniques, your child is in a **time-in** whenever he is not in **time-out.**

Are You Inspired?

At this point in the process, you may have experienced many successes. We assume you've done your best to create successful moments with your child and are building a relationship based on time-in and time-out within a clear and concrete structure. BRAVO!

Take a moment to reflect on the changes you have seen since you began this journey. What has shifted? In what ways do you feel more connected to your child? Are you viewing him/her differently? How has this approach changed other relationships in your life?

_____

_____

_____

_____

_____

Nurture Your Way to Transformation...

Bobby, an 8-year old raised in a home where there was significant substance abuse on the part of both parents, frequently witnessed physical abuse of his mother by his father and later toward subsequent girlfriends after Bobby's mother left the home. Bobby would hide in his room when the abuse was occurring.

Local social service officers removed Bobby from his home and he was placed with experienced, skilled foster parents who took him to a child therapist. When the therapist first saw him, Bobby refused to make eye contact and would not speak. He was in fights on the school bus and in the classroom, and it had been necessary to remove him from both those environments at times for choking others. He constantly argued with adults as well as with peers, particularly with his younger sister, toward whom he was also physically aggressive. Bobby threatened violence toward others, and he was observed to be highly impulsive, inattentive and demanding. His foster parents described him as a "sad little boy" with a "doom and gloom" outlook.

Luckily, Bobby's new therapist was familiar with The Nurtured Heart Approach. She began working with Bobby once weekly, and his foster parents established a program heavy with acknowledgements, appreciations and clear rules and boundaries. Within a few weeks, Bobby began making eye contact, smiling and laughing. His ability to pay attention improved. His behavior improved, both at home and at school. He was able to ride the bus with no fear of being removed. He was in a regular classroom and a regular seat, with peers seated to each side of him. Bobby began to make positive self-statements, suggesting he was internalizing his newfound successes.

Four months after Bobby came to live with them, his foster parents commented, "This is not the same child." **They had begun to see Bobby in light of who he really is.** Although Bobby still has a way to go, they plan to continue The Nurtured Heart Approach, slowly building the new portfolio that will strengthen Bobby internally. There is hope for his future!

In The Nurtured Heart Approach, time-outs are separations of connection and relationship. During time-out, the child is missing out on life's energy and life's options – missing out on life's payoffs. Setting limits by way of time-outs is the mechanism to re-establish connection and get the relationship back to a successful one.

Nurtured Heart time-outs are usually easy and short. In most instances they need only be a matter of seconds because *any separation of relationship* is a time-out. By keeping the consequence short, the end is in sight for the child AND for the parent. In this approach, time-in is the heart of the awakening. Time-ins are the flow of energy and relationship in connection with a *sense of success*. That sets the stage for the consequences to really have an impact. When you energize success at a greater level, you are connecting with your child in the most enjoyable, beneficial, and positive way. Essentially, the time-in happens whenever the child is not in time-out – i.e., all the times when you are recognizing successes and eventually when the process internalizes and the child perceives her own successfulness.

If time-ins are insignificant to the child, time-outs will have no effect whatsoever. In contrast, if time-ins have a sufficient impact, time-outs can move mountains. Time-in functions as the psychological and emotional nutrition that flows when things are going right and not going wrong. When time-ins are highly energized and consistently in place, then you are ready to roll with the consequence phase.

Time-ins are the flow of energy and relationship in connection with a *sense of success*.

Limit Setting/Delivering Consequences

By experiencing energized success – the Active, Experiential, Proactive and Creative Recognitions that result in the powerful time-ins – the child now knows exactly what happens in the way of being appreciated when rules are NOT broken.

These strategies have begun to shift the child into new modes of productive energy use. They are designed to make the child aware that it is not necessary to go to the trouble of pursuing negative attention because she is literally surrounded by positive attention and it is readily available. That, coupled with the fact that the child now knows the rules in a much clearer way, is what sets the stage for delivering consequences.

Giving consequences that are simple is one secret.

Remember that the road toward transformation involves energizing successes and withdrawing our energy from problem behaviors. In The Nurtured Heart Approach, then, the secret is *giving consequences that are simple and consistent but that do not energize negativity.*

"Getting out of the way" and allowing the child to experience the simple consequences is another secret.

It is vitally important to learn to get out of the way and allow the child to experience the simple consequence and discover that she will no longer get our energy for rule-breaking and negativity, that there is no longer anything to be gained by breaking the rule, and that the big reactions are now for the positive behaviors and choices.

How do we get out of the way and allow the child to have a clearer version of consequences than ever before? The answer is everything we've said up to now:

1. Always giving the consequence when a rule is broken.

2. *Consistently, day-after-day,* NOT looking the other way.

3. Delivering the consequence in a very neutral manner.

4. Keeping the consequence short and very simple.

5. Avoiding warnings.

6. Energizing success after the consequence is served.

7. Making time-in energetically powerful.

Keeping these things in mind, the fact of the matter is that kids know the secret. They know we cannot stop them from breaking the rules. Getting out of the way is allowing them the freedom to break the rules. When we give them this freedom, it allows them to choose to follow the rules. They discover that there is no longer any attachment to breaking the rules and parents are no longer afraid of their kids breaking the rules.

The Proof Is In The Pudding...

Co-author Lisa Bravo tells this story to illustrate the point: *One day I picked my son up from school and noticed he was visibly upset. When I asked him what was wrong, he began to cry and said he got a "red day" at school today. A "red day" is the pinnacle of bad within his classroom. It meant he had to 1) turn his name over on the discipline wall in front of his class, and 2) bring a note home to his parents and write an apology. In his third-grade world, this was completely overwhelming.*

My first instinct was to ask a barrage of questions about what he did or why he did it, but instead I took a deep breath and consciously decided to get out of the way and say nothing. Within a few seconds, Christopher was talking aloud to himself, saying, "OK, it's just a blip on the screen, all I have is a consequence, tomorrow is a new day." He continued to take deep breaths until he was calm.

Even though he was upset, he was able to process the facts and modulate his emotional response – a true testament to how this approach helps children internalize healthy coping skills. My role was to praise him for all these great skills he was now showing despite his day at school.

By the way…even kids on medication know how to break the rules.

Howard Glasser recalls the following incident. Parents who had brought their daughter to his practice because of behavior problems at some point stated that, since the child was just put on medication, the poor behavior was gone. The parents attributed the child's subsequent good choices and improved impulse control to the medication.

Howie then turned to the daughter and asked, "Nora, do you know *how* to break the rules?"

"Well, yes," she stammered.

"If you wanted to break the rules right now, even though you are on medications, could you?" asked Howie.

"Of course, I could," she said.

In that moment, Howie exposed an important truth. Even if a child is on medication, it is important to recognize that, when he is making good choices, it is because he consciously has chosen NOT to break the rules. Children know the secret that we often overlook: they always have a choice and they can always break a rule anytime they wish. That is why it is so crucial to appreciate when they don't. **The medication didn't decide – the CHILD decided.**

Resetting to Greatness...

Be creative. Use "RESET," "PAUSE" or whatever language works for your child. Remember, it's NOT about being punitive. It's about inserting a momentary break so that you can return to energizing success. The child will feel it as a consequence and you will feel it as a call to action to appreciate the greatness that unfolds in the next nows.

Letting the child have a simple experience of a true consequence can bring him to the awareness that "the old game isn't working."

At some point in time, the light dawns! The child arrives at a moment of truth, drawing her own conclusion that it is her decision whether or not to break a rule. The child finally understands that the way to obtain our energy is by NOT breaking rules or behaving in an adverse manner. The message here is that it is okay to break rules. It is not the parent's job to stop the rule breaking. We all have freedom to break rules, and our children also are free to do so. Why not "get out of the way" and allow the child to come to the moment of truth that it's her option as to whether or not a rule is broken?

Time-outs/resets are delivered unceremoniously and without emotional expression.

In The Nurtured Heart Approach, a time-out is the sole consequence for any broken rule. Time-outs are delivered unceremoniously and without emotional expression when a rule is broken to the slightest degree. Most parents say either "That's a broken rule" or "That's a time-out" and walk away. Never engage in any discussion, explanation or sermon but simply deliver the consequence each time. Sermons are not delivered in an adverse situation because they reward the negativity. **Time-outs can be performed in a designated area, or adults can levy a time-out merely by turning or walking away (i.e., breaking connection).**

A truly effective consequence interrupts the pattern of misbehavior and moves the child to a place where poor choices lose their appeal. This is the kind of consequence that works in the context of the Nurtured Heart Approach: **the clean time-out,** which we've come to refer to almost exclusively as a **reset**.

Call it a time-out, a pause, a chill pill, or a break; no matter what term you use, it is a time-out from connectivity, relationship and interaction that lasts no more than a minute or so but can also be over in two seconds flat.

What it looks like when your children are comfortable with your new style of parenting:

- They are more motivated to follow rules.

- They are more confident.

- They begin to put themselves in time-out.

- They catch themselves <u>before</u> they act impulsively.

- They have fewer mood swings.

- They are more aware of the success of those around them and they want to celebrate it.

- They begin to provide active recognition for others around them.

- They make and keep more friends.

- They become more adept at conflict resolution.

- They trust themselves to rely on their internal wisdom to make good choices for themselves.

- They see the world as an exciting, positive place with boundless opportunities.

Time-outs/resets are short.

In The Nurtured Heart Approach, consequences or time-outs do not look the same as typically suggested in most parenting methods. We do not subscribe to the commonly held notion of giving a child a minute of time-out per year of age. Why?

Because time-outs are merely the mechanism to allow a shift in the negative behavior and then an immediate return to the relentless barrage of recognizing successes. Time-outs/resets may be no longer than it takes to turn your back: as few as two seconds or up to one minute. We prefer the word 'reset' because it implies a pause, a re-entry into time-in that has a quality of restoration. You, the parent, get to decide when time-out has been served well and is over. The good news is you don't need your timer anymore!

In time, your child will make the connection between her personal sense of responsibility and how her choices affect the outcome.

Time-outs are always energized after they have been successfully served.

A time-out provides the opportunity to create and point out more success; therefore, energizing the success of its having been completed always follows a time-out. Why? Even if the child resisted time-out and you had to struggle to get him to do it, the fact is that somehow, some way he eventually calmed down enough to complete the consequence. That needs to be commended!

If you are dying to give a sermon, NOW is the time, after the time-out and only in conjunction with the follow-up time-in. The sound of your NEW sermon: "Brad, thanks for serving your time-out well. I notice that right now you are being respectful. Even though you have strong feelings, you are not yelling anymore, or calling me names. Right now your behavior is telling me that you can handle a tough conversation."

A time-out is an opportunity to relay to the child that you trust him to be able to handle his feelings no matter what they are. An appropriately delivered time-out also sends a message to your child that you, yourself, can handle your feelings – your anger – and that the momentary disruption in relationship can be restored. In that manner, the child will know he does not have to live in fear of your anger. Conversely you do not have to live in fear of his adverse behavior.

What to do when your child blows up or threatens.

Always stick with the plan. Feel your feelings, but keep them private. DO NOT: lecture, argue, apologize, promise seek, reprimand, weep, swear, yell, discuss or negotiate. Just say, "Time-out begins when you are quiet." Then turn away or walk away. If the child says, "Leave me alone" or anything else negative or disrespectful, keep your voice quality as normal as possible and stay calm. Just say "Time-out begins when you are quiet." Be sure to energize success after the time-out is completed by saying something like, "Andy, you sat so well through that time-out. I appreciate that you were able to accept the consequences of breaking a rule, even though you were angry with me for deciding you needed one. That's a wonderful decision you made!"

The truth is, your child could have upped the ante and remained angry for hours but didn't. WE need to recognize and stay tuned in to the truth of the moments as they unfold.

Time-outs/Resets: Going Deeper

To give a consequence, simply say the child's name, then say, "Reset" or "Time-out." As soon as the rule-breaking stops, welcome the child back and give appreciation for a reset well done and for the rules now being followed and positive values and qualities being demonstrated by this choice. You can accuse the child of resetting for any de-escalation, moment of silence or movement toward more positive choices. At times, your child won't know he or she has reset until you tell him or her she's done so successfully!

The power of this consequence has nothing to do with its length. The power of the reset comes from two sources: first, from the child's sense of missing out on the new realm of time-in and ever more strongly wanting to get back to his growing sense of successfulness; and second, from *refusing to accidentally energize negativity* while illuminating successes in the moments that follow the reset. This illumination is achieved by way of comments that heighten the growing edge of the child's progressing inner wealth. It is the perfect confluence of the rivers of NO and YES.

Virtually *every consequence* most people can think of amounts to a time-out in the end. Consider the major categories of consequences used by most parents: 1) loss of privileges, and 2) restitution. When a child loses a privilege, she's out of the loop of life. Whether you call that a time-out or not, her deepest experience is that of a time-out. Restitution might entail community service, tasks, or extra work. This, too, boils down to a time-out from the action. A child sent to the principal's office or enduring a lecture about her misdeeds is as well. All of these consequences remove the child from the time-in of access to the world of possibilities.

Once the reset is given, watch like a hawk for any movement in the direction of stopping the unwanted behavior: even a simple pause can be sufficient. Once that happens, even for a moment, get right back to creating successes, starting with an acknowledgement that the reset has been completed.

A reset is a reminder that all the 'juice' of relationship happens when rules are being followed. It works only if the parent or teacher resolves to have *no emotional attachment to children following the rules*—or, at least, to remove themselves from the situation if they need to vent or process emotions that would energize the child's rule-breaking. Another option: to divert the raw emotional energy that would previously have been unleashed in the form of frustration or anger into warrior-like determination to energize the good stuff!

Once you grasp that acting out is really just an unconscious ploy to try to get connected with the gift of YOU, it becomes easier to refuse to react in an emotionally hurt or angered way to rule-breaking. Once you have this dynamic figured out, you're in a much more advantageous position. However: **safety always comes first!** When someone's safety is at stake, do whatever is necessary to de-escalate the situation. Then, get your three stands working again as soon as possible. Let physical violence or destruction of property be a signal to you to take Stands One and Two up a few notches. Then, set up some form of restoration that will enable the child to make up for the infraction, but that is void of discussion and energy; for example, some form of community service.

Make resets predictable and boring. Be as vacant and detached as the police officer who writes a ticket and says, "Have a nice day." *Get out of the way* until the child exhausts her repertoire of excuses, machinations and ploys. Every instance of rule-breaking is a chance for you to demonstrate that things have changed: that accountability happens without the old sidecar of relationship, and that relationship now happens only around success.

If a child flatly refuses to do the reset, one option is to keep withholding energy as you wait for the issue to pass. Then, purposefully create the illusion of the reset having been completed. Do this by simply accusing the child of successfully resetting and moving on to the next acknowledgement of success.

When giving resets, avoid energizing negativity and maintain clarity by:

- Delivering plenty of positives to other children who are following the rules. It's all too easy to get to a place where you end up putting out disciplinary fires and losing out on chances to energize positives.
- Refusing to allow a child who's in a reset to make any contribution to whatever's going on.
- Refusing to explain the "why" of the time-out.
- Refusing to take offense at rule-breaking.
- Refusing to shame/humiliate the rule-breaker.
- Refusing to use warnings or redirections instead of resets.
- Refusing to give a time-out in anticipation of rule-breaking that has not yet occurred.
- Refusing to make exceptions to the rules for children who have "special needs." Expecting the child with ADHD, learning disabilities, or other handicaps to follow the same essential rules as all others is of huge benefit. The child comes to accept that

she is responsible for her own conduct and that she can adhere to the rules; and that when she chooses to do so, she gets plenty of relationship and respect from you.

- Refusing to let your energy related to the child's negativity be detected by the child. Instead, choose to feel your feelings internally, using the energy of those feelings as fuel to re-commit to your Stands.

What To Do In Public

Delivering a consequence or time-out when you are in public is often a tricky proposition. Your intense child is likely to respond more intensely when there is an audience. We recommend that when you are out together, stick with the plan, continue to create and build success, and be careful not to let your guard down. Avoid warnings and give swift, clear time-outs. Remember, you no longer have to find a spot to do a traditional time-out. It can take place in just a few seconds. If your child refuses to do a time-out, simply explain that she will have her consequence when she gets home.

There is no need to beg or plead. Just calmly say, "that's time-out at home" and walk away. Avoid the temptation to lecture, plead or beg for the behavior to change.

Time-outs for older children and adolescents.

Short time-outs are also used for older children and adolescents. Just move away and the child will perceive he is not in the game. At the point when he approaches you, energize the success by saying something like, "Thank you for choosing to observe your time-out; that showed good character." If there had been a request prior to the time-out, then add: "Now, I need you to do the chore I told you to do." For severe or bigger rules violations, particularly with a teen, community service can be part of the consequence. (This is discussed more specifically under Credit Systems.)

Remember: No conversation.
We are not going to fall apart.
We are utterly determined to wait it out.

How to Present Consequences to the Child

Once you have begun using the acknowledgements and appreciations of this approach and are refusing to energize negativity, the stage is set to present the idea of consequences to the child.

By virtue of the recognitions (time-ins) you are now using with your child, she probably is already breaking fewer rules. If that's the case, take this opportunity to explain to your child that she is showing improvements. Acknowledge her growing ability to follow rules. Tell her that, from now on, if a rule is broken, there will be a short time-out. Be clear and neutral despite your child's reaction to this announcement. Explain that because things are going so much better, the consequences will be much simpler and easier to complete. (If you are using a credit system, explained in the next chapter, let her know that you will continue to give credits and chances to earn more privileges for following the rules, but there will still be time-outs for rule-breaking.)

Below are the steps for presenting the concept of consequences to the child.

1. Describe the Time-Out Process to the Child

Make it especially clear that every time he breaks a rule, there will be a short time-out.

For example, say: *"Now every time you break a rule, there will be a short time-out. I can't really stop you from breaking rules, can I? I can't stop you from name calling or yelling. I can't really stop you from arguing or refusing to do something. I have made it clear that it is always your choice. I can, though, give you a consequence every time you decide to break a rule.*

It's kind of like basketball – if you step out-of-bounds just a little bit, it's a consequence. The good news is I won't be fussing, lecturing, taking away privileges, giving extra chores or any of those things I used to do in the past. You have the right to break the rules. You just need to know what's going to happen when you do break a rule."

Or say: *"You know, you've been doing a much better job using self-control and not breaking rules. Let's just come up with a consequence that is simple and easy so that we know in advance what happens when you do break a rule. Here's what I have I mind. From now on, if you decide to break a rule, even just a little bit, we will give you a short time-out. We will no longer ground you, yell at you or punish you. You'll just get a time-out every time you decide to break a rule. In other words, it's your option to follow the rules, and if you do, we will do our best to continue to be appreciative."*

When you are using a seated time-out for a younger child you should add: *"If you don't go to time-out right away when you are told, then I will take you to time-out. Also, if you decide to get out of the chair, I will hold you there."*

If you decide not to use a time-out chair, explain the method you've chosen to use for time-outs – perhaps just walking away until you decide to return and call the end to the time-out.

For an older child who is too big to escort or hold in time-out and for whom you are already using a credit system, or plan to, also add: *"If you don't go to time-out when you are told, then this is what will happen until you decide to do it: I will continue to give you credits for all your good behaviors. Your credits will be frozen, however, until the time-out is completed. In other words, you will continue to get credits but won't be able to spend any because basically the store is closed until you get around to completing your time-out. Then you can begin spending again."*

2. Explain What Happens When Time-Outs are Given Out of the Home

For example say: *"If we are away from home, you will either take your time-out there or as soon as we get home. If you refuse to take your time-out when we're away, then it will be a double time-out when we get home. It's* up to you. In other words, you can break all the rules you like, but this is what will happen when you do."

> Remember the video game example from the first section of the book? The game gives the child permission to break the rules in the same way that time-out does with Nurtured Heart parenting. And guess what happens? The child becomes BETTER at NOT breaking the rules. Giving the freedom to break the rules allows the child to reinvent herself in a sensational way. She learns of her own volition to work with the rules. She comes to realize that she is not being asked to be perfect!

3. Emphasize the "No-Warning" Rule

Say, "There will be no warnings, reminders or second chances when you break a rule now. I'll just say 'That's a time-out,' and you will be expected to take your time-out right away on your own."

4. Emphasize Reset Compliance and Give Incentives

For a younger child, say, "Reset. I'll let you know when you're done." Be prepared to hijack the child into a successful reset. You can also choose to offer an incentive of credits if the reset is done without a fuss.

For an older child, say: "Reset. I will tell you when your time is done." If you are using a credit system, you can add: "If you reset well, you can earn bonus credits." If the child resists and a credit system is in use, let the child know ahead of time that credits will always be frozen until resets are completed

5. Explain How the Timekeeping of Time-Out Works

Say: "I will start timing your time-out as soon as you are quiet and I will tell you when it is completed." We do not advise that you talk about duration of time-outs. It does not help the child. Rather, you watch the time and keep it on the short side. We highly recommend using your internal sense of what a time-out should be. Most people hold it to a matter of seconds. Time-out begins as soon as the child settles down. Remember, it's not the length of time-out or the severity of the punishment that creates the awakening. The goal is to ultimately convince the child that he can live a full and fruitful existence in the realm of successfulness. The child comes to feel that he can wrap his intensity and life force around this new way of being in the world. That's the *awakening!*

The Battle of Wills

When disciplining your child becomes a power struggle, it is important to reset your own button. The goal is to disengage from the dynamic of power and control. The way to do that is by taking a stand **NOT to engage in negativity or reward negativity at all!** Although it may be tempting in the heat of the moment, remain strong in your conviction. The more you resist this counterproductive pattern of interacting, the more you change the relationship into one that is engaging and desirable.

6. Explain That You Will Not Talk With the Child During Time-Out or Answer Questions

Say: *"I will not talk with you during time-out or answer questions. I'm also not going to make you promise to never do it again or discuss the problem with you after the time-out is over. Later, if you want some help thinking through solutions or other ways to handle a situation, let me know."*

Helpful Tips

Not explaining the infraction allows the child a "purer" experience of the consequence of breaking a specific rule.

We strongly encourage you to resist the temptation to deliver a masterful lecture before, during or after a reset. This will only undermine your Stand of refusing to energize the negative. A much better alternative that we now recommend is to give the "sermon," so to speak, AFTER the time-out by way of reflecting the actual successes of the ensuing next moments.

Recognize that the child is now back in the game (time-in) by accusing him of NOT breaking the rules. For example, if Lenny was in time-out for hitting, the optimal time to deliver the sermon is when the time-out is over and the child is being successful. "Lenny, you are not hitting right now. That shows you are respecting the rules."

Do not fall into a discussion of whether or not a rule was really broken.

Discussing whether or not the problem behavior was a broken rule can lead to an ENORMOUS payoff of your energy and relationship. Like the referee in sports, YOU are the one to decide if the infraction was a broken rule. Therefore, merely state that the rule was broken and then pronounce the consequence.

Time-outs need to be devoid of verbal or nonverbal reaction, lectures or hints of how it affected you emotionally.

This again gives your child a payoff in relation to the broken rule. Remember to remain neutral and do not let your emotions show. In addition, use of timers or responding to demands of "when is time-out over?" can easily become a little cat and mouse situation. Also, refrain from comments like "If only you will quiet down, time-out could begin," or other such pleas or reminders. **Avoid getting drawn into the drama for any reason whatsoever. It will only energize the negativity and perpetuate the show.**

Remain unflappable! This is where the rubber meets the road.

A younger child might try to get out of resetting by asking for a drink of water or to use the bathroom. Your refusal might put you to the ultimate test as the child urinates, spits, defecates or vomits - lengths to which the most intense young children might sometimes go to test this new dynamic. Older children might escalate in other ways. Even in the face of this kind of resistance, stay calm, strong and firm (while keeping in mind that safety is always first!). Calmly, firmly have the child clean up any messes and create opportunities for restitution for other infractions. Once the child sees that the old ploys no longer work, turnaround is right around the corner. Resistance is a typically a sign that progress has been significant and the old patterns are about to fall away.

Do not allow any interruptions during the time-out.

Do not permit other children or individuals to interfere with completion of the time-out. Siblings should be told to stay away and not talk to, taunt or otherwise bother the child in time-out. It's also helpful to have a rule against fiddling or playing with anything during a reset. Use your best judgment, however, to avoid aiming for military-style perfection, which won't further your cause.

It's really a leap of faith – go into it believing it will work. For many of us, implementing this approach is a lot more challenging than anticipated. There will be ups and downs, testing, and moments that feel uncomfortable. Remember, a little faith goes a long way when it comes to learning a new way of parenting. Be patient with yourself and HAVE FAITH!

Have time-out, will travel...

ONE more time: It doesn't matter WHERE the time-out occurs nearly as much as the MESSAGE IT SENDS. The point is, you have the ability to send the message to your child at any moment. Remember, it can happen in a mere few seconds of taking the child "out of the game." If you are more comfortable with a defined space for time-out, go for it, but remember that you do have options.

Time-Out to Go

Justin, a 14-year old boy, would often misbehave when the family was out in public. His mother would keep track of time-outs owed and have him serve them when they returned home. Justin would have to sit in "the chair" until all of his time-outs were served. This would often lead to a power struggle with Justin disputing how many rules he had broken and how much chair time he owed. There was a lot of energy being given to negativity and the time-out as it was being implemented had become counterproductive.

Justin and his parents got into a cycle of negativity that did little to get him back into successful moments. His parents were at their wit's end and knew that what they were doing was not working. Justin was getting all sorts of payoffs *energetically* for breaking the rules. To demonstrate this to his parents, co-author Lisa Bravo turned to Justin and asked a couple of questions: "Justin, do you *know* when you are breaking a rule?" He shook his head in affirmation. She then asked, "Have your parents ever put you in time-out when you did not have any idea why?" Justin looked at Lisa and said, "No."

This was an "AH HA moment" for Justin's parents. They now understood that it did not matter WHERE the time-out occurred, it mattered WHEN it occurred. They learned that "in the moment" time-outs left a stronger impression than delaying the consequence until they were at home and had access to the chair. Time-outs delivered on-the-spot and unceremoniously left little room for accidentally feeding negativity and they were able to get back into energizing successes right away. When his parents changed this aspect of their parenting, the relationship began to shift and the awakening started!

A Note on The Nurtured Heart Approach and Physical Punishments

It has been our experience that the vast majority of parents who use physical punishments, such as spanking, do not use it with an abusive intent or a desire to damage the spirit of the child, but rather out of frustration to find something that works. We are opposed to physical punishments for many reasons. For purposes of this continued examination, the salient fact is that they will backfire strategically.

One danger in the use of physical punishment is that the child becomes truly confused about whether it is a reward or a punishment. Children addicted to getting negative attention elicit a huge payoff in terms of the parents' level of reaction and relationship. Although they hate being hit and might be frightened, they still feel the rush of having pushed a button big time – with a big payoff of connection and intimacy. The "toy" really gets animated.

At the same time, children sense when their parents are out of control. They unfortunately continue to test until convinced that the parents can maintain a calm and healthy level of control.

Children need their parents to be powerful in healthy and balanced ways because that is a primary way in which they learn to have their own healthy power. This is particularly important for intense children.

In addition, the use of physical punishment does nothing to resolve relationship issues and likely even exacerbates them. That is, physical punishment might stop the behavior temporarily, but it does not resolve the core problem within the underlying relationship. Physical punishment is counter-productive to what you are trying to achieve.

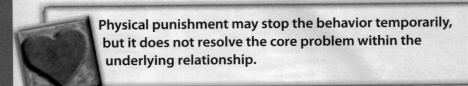

Physical punishment may stop the behavior temporarily, but it does not resolve the core problem within the underlying relationship.

So, what's wrong with a spanking every now and then?

We have worked with thousands of children over the past three decades. Some parents have used spankings as a discipline tool. The majority of these parents had good intentions and believed they were teaching their children important lessons in these moments. However, very few parents can honestly say they have never spanked their child when frustrated or angry. Many have admitted to hitting harder than they intended and feeling out of control. When one attempt doesn't work, it's not unusual to move to increasingly more severe versions.

In The Nurtured Heart Approach, we NEVER recommend spanking as a form of discipline because it feeds negativity and does not provide emotional nutrition for the child. It does not promote emotional connection and energizing successes. In a backwards way, the child sees it as a reward of energy. There is a big payoff by way of the child's perception of receiving time, emotion and connection in relation to his poor choices. The child comes to realize that his poor choice once again has led to more $100 bills!

Spanking to teach a lesson never works because the brain is literally unable to process information logically when it is in a state of arousal. In recent years, there have been numerous studies about this subject. The portion of the brain that controls logic and reasoning, the cerebral cortex, becomes less active, and the limbic system, or emotional brain, becomes the most active. Did you ever try to reason with someone who is extremely upset? Notice how they are unable to discuss how and why they are feeling a certain way until they have calmed down. During a spanking and shortly after, the child is literally unable to process or learn.

12 Good Reasons to be Concerned About Spanking:

1. Spanking sends many confusing messages – emotionally, cognitively, viscerally, relationally, and spiritually.
2. It does not provide emotional nutrition.
3. It teaches the child that it is okay to hurt others when we are angry, offended, frustrated, or feeling out of control.
4. It erodes the connection and trust between parent and child.
5. It models hitting and is likely to be replicated with siblings and peers.
6. It does not resolve the underlying problem.
7. It often makes the parent feel more upset and more hopeless.
8. It does not improve behavior, especially over the long-term.
9. It teaches ineffective coping skills.
10. It teaches children that it is acceptable to use power and control to get what is wanted.
11. It often fosters aggressive behaviors and acting out long after the spanking has occurred.
12. It is not necessary if the first two phases of The Nurtured Heart Approach are being adequately implemented.

Playing Hardball

Parents who previously tried and failed at traditional ways of playing hardball – often out of frustration resorting to escalating bouts of yelling, threats and physical punishments – report that The Nurtured Heart Approach actually felt like a better version of hardball that really worked. One reason is that they never have to look the other way or give warnings. The line is the line, and even a tiny bit of broken rule is a broken rule. There's always accountability. They always deliver and they no longer accidentally reward negativity. That's another way to play hardball. No more $100 bills rewarding adversity. The new and best way of playing hardball is in creating successes left and right – refusing to forget.

These parents understand that this is the way to win the war. They're becoming warriors of success.

Fact or Fiction?

There has been extensive research on the effects of corporal punishment over the past two decades. This is what the research shows:

- Corporal punishment teaches violence and revenge as a way to solve problems. Adults who were hit as children are statistically more likely to be depressed or violent. (Burkowitz, 1993)

- Children who get spanked regularly are more likely to cheat or lie, disobey at school, bully others, and show less remorse for wrong-doing. (Straus, Sugarman, Giles-Sims, 1997)

- Corporal punishment in childhood is often a predictor of later antisocial behavior traits. (Gunhoe & Mariner, 1997)

- Corporal punishment adversely affects cognitive development. Children who are spanked perform poorly on school tasks compared to other children. (Straus & Mather, 1995; Strauss & Paschall, 1998)

- Parents most often use corporal punishment as a way to gain compliance, but the research shows that it has an opposite and undesired long-term effect. (Straus & Donnelly, 2001)

- There is a correlation between being spanked as a child and later problems associated with anxiety, depression and substance abuse. (McMillan, 1995)

- Spanking has no measurable beneficial effects at all and is associated with a variety of long-term negative effects. (Straus & Donnelly, 2001)

What's become obvious to us as clinicians over the years is that, despite ideologies that support spanking – whether religious or personal – there is high potential for risk. Do we really want to take that chance?

Our answer is that The Nurtured Heart Approach provides you, the parents, with a **new set of strategies** that fosters healthy leverage you might not have had in the past. These strategies work and they offer you an opportunity to abandon the risk of old techniques forever.

The "Spare the Rod" Controversy

There has been ongoing confusion and debate about certain verses in the Bible. Consider the time in which the Bible was written. The "rod," "staff" or "shebet" was a vital tool for the shepherd. It was used to fight off prey in the pastures, but more often it was used to guide wandering or lost sheep back into the fold. The hook of the staff was placed around the neck of the sheep and used to gently but firmly pull them back to the group and to safety. Shepherds took care of and valued their sheep; they would not have dreamed of hurting them.

If we look at the verses within this context, it makes sense. As parents, we are to "shepherd" our children by protecting them and keeping them safe. If they stray, it is our job to lead them back to us in a gentle but firm manner. We believe The Nurtured Heart Approach fully embodies the intent of these revered passages.

The Wrap Up

• Begin the consequence phase only after the success techniques are in motion.

• **CONTINUE** to give all the different forms of positive recognition and appreciation that you have learned. Be an opportunist and praise the control and power the child uses when handling strong feelings well, and, as much as possible, for not breaking the rules.

• Having decided that it is time to initiate consequences, immediately begin the use of time-outs as the sole consequence for any broken rule. You are no longer ignoring broken rules. You are holding the child accountable every time he crosses the line. The truth is, it IS a big success when the child completes the consequence for poor behavior.

The Wrap Up – Continued

- Short time-outs are powerful. It is not the length of the time-out but its **connection to the event** and **your clear attitude** that matter. Time-outs are not, and do not have to be, lengthy. Do NOT use the old time-out rule of one minute for every year of age. They can be as short as 10 to 15 seconds. They begin when the child is in the designated place and is quiet.

- If the child goes directly and quietly to the time-out chair or area, begin right away. Remember, **no consoling, lecturing or talking** when the child is in time-out. Keep siblings and others away.

- Award credit points or a shorter time-out if the time-out goes smoothly and without incident. **Completion of time-out is a success!**

- Remember to reinforce successful completion of a consequence or time-out. Get right back to positives (time-in) as soon as the consequence is over.

- After the time-out, the child should be required to clean up any messes made prior to or during it and **complete any tasks resisted or unfinished** before time-out.

- Remember to apply the rule "No disobeying," both for purposes of positive reinforcement and for situations where requests are met with non-compliance.

- Don't expect remorse or other displays of conscience from the child. Trust that you are indeed having an effect despite the possible lack of immediate results or direct feedback. Continue realistically linking choices and results by pointing out successes.

The Wrap Up – Continued

- Do not request apologies or promises from the child never to do the transgression again. Once time-out ends, resist the urge to mediate the problem or discuss how the child might have done things differently. All of these still energetically fuel the very problem that you want to stop. In contrast, **see the child doing it differently** and acknowledge **that** as a success.

- For the more difficult child, give more frequent appreciations, with more detail and more voltage.

The Next Step

We are now ready to move on to the next phase of The Nurtured Heart Approach, which is the Credit System.

CHAPTER 4

Phase III:
The Credit System

Not all families need a credit system for the approach to be successful. The first phases of the approach are highly transformative in their own right. However, we have found three primary reasons to use a credit system:

1. If the child is having problems at school and the school's policies are not helping the child to succeed;

2. If you are less than confident in your ability to remember to be appreciative on a consistent basis;

3. If you really desire to get your child to sit in a time-out chair and you need leverage to do so.

The credit system works well, particularly for these above circumstances.

Some Cautions about Using a Credit System

Not every child needs a credit system. Our experience is that it will make sense and be "doable" for some but not for others. Further, do not attempt a credit system if you are not committed to it 100 percent of the time for as long as you need. Typically, for it to work, you need to expect that it will take a little extra time to design the system, to explain it to your child, and to sit down with the child at the end of every day for review.

In The Nurtured Heart Approach, the credit system is a highly organized way to facilitate, reinforce and encourage success – a method to strengthen what is already in motion as a result of creative recognitions. The basic concepts of energizing success and not energizing adversity or negativity are *always* foundational aspects of The Nurtured Heart Approach – they are *never* left out, and they are continued in the credit system. The credit system provides an opportunity to add to the child's positive portfolio. It systematically captures the child being successful. Never use the credit system as a punishment in disguise; this will only add to the child's negative portfolio.

The credit system is always presented *after success has been experienced with the creative recognition techniques* and should be implemented once Phase I has been somewhat established. It is intended to be used in concert with the techniques. The Nurtured Heart credit system does not use candy, toys or other treats as rewards. Instead, it rewards children with psychological and emotional nutrition, the powerful energy that is conveyed through statements of gratitude in response to positive choices. In The Nurtured Heart Approach, the credit system is not tedious or laborious. Rather, when you set up a credit system, you are creating a custom-made, heart-centered "video game," tailor-made to your child's needs and abilities.

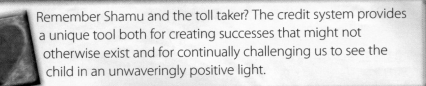

Remember Shamu and the toll taker? The credit system provides a unique tool both for creating successes that might not otherwise exist and for continually challenging us to see the child in an unwaveringly positive light.

In this game, however, you decide the rules, you award the credits, and believe it or not, your child will not only want to play, but he will want to play at increasingly more challenging and successful levels. The question then is, how do we arrive at this point? First, we will discuss the principles of the credit system and then describe how to design and implement such a system.

Principles of the Credit System

A credit system is a "resource exchange" system.

Every human being is in the same boat. We are all faced with the need to manage our economy. We all exchange credits in an economy. In essence, we are *all* on a credit system and have to learn to live in an economy. Rich, poor, working, retired, we all rely on our resources to get the things we need and want. Even the panhandler on the street corner has an economy and is on a credit system. His necessities may include a candy bar and a pack of cigarettes, while ours are typically more extensive (job, home, vehicle, etc.).

For adults, credit systems are first-hand experiences.

As adults, we already know the details, nuances and idiosyncrasies of our system. We know the realities of what we have to do to obtain our resources. And we also know the realities of allocating what we have so that we can meet our needs. This is a first-hand experience for us on a daily basis.

Many challenging children have a lopsided picture of the way the world works and are not prepared for the real-life economy they will face.

Challenging children in particular have more distortion in their 'lens field.' That distortion says, "When I screw up, I get more attention and privileges." These children have a stronger sense of entitlement and are accustomed to 'railroading' people. They are proficient at being entitled. Unfortunately, that will not serve them well unless they have a throne. What they have is a lopsided picture of the way the real world works.

*The credit system provides a
modern-day apprenticeship of the economy
children will someday face.*

The credit system can function as an apprenticeship of real life. It can help the child learn how the world really works and help her be better prepared for our real life economy. It teaches wise handling of money, negotiating, bargaining and other useful economic techniques. Typical allowance systems and chore systems fall short because they are not encompassing enough to teach the child how the world *really* works.

It's Really All Encompassing...

As adults, our credit system is all encompassing. We pay for water, food, electricity, gasoline, shelter, and most other needs. Simply asking a child to rake the leaves for money does little to get children to understand the encompassing nature of our real economy. A credit system that focuses on chores and allowances does not adequately prepare the child for the system they will encounter as adults.

*The first-hand experiences of adults are,
for children, a second-hand experience.*

Children essentially experience *our* experiences, but for them, they are second-hand experiences. Children do not understand all the economic realities and requirements of daily life – the extent of the costs that we parents incur. They do not absorb the dynamics and depth of an economy unless it is taught directly by enveloping them in a first-hand experience.

The credit system is a marvelous opportunity to reinforce and encourage success continuously on a daily basis, and over time it leads to development of inner wealth.

An organized and steady stream of successes provides a strong level of emotional nutrition and leads to trust. The credit system advances the idea of perpetuity of emotional nutrition. It allows the child choice and positive regard. This sets the child on a path toward development of inner wealth. Kids with a sense of economy and healthy inner wealth gracefully make the transition to real life. Those who do not have a sense of economy or inner wealth can have a very difficult time dealing with real life.

We've mentioned inner wealth before – here's another way of saying the same thing: Inner wealth is coming to perceive and KNOW the truth about one's core being in a progressively more razor-sharp way. That is in contrast to not knowing or being vague and doubtful about the truth of one's greatness. One who has any degree of vagueness about his greatness will not be able to use his intensity as well.

Time-outs as well as school behaviors can be enhanced through a credit system.

The credit system is useful for parents who have decided to require a seated time-out for their child because they can use the leverage of the credits being temporarily unavailable for spending to influence the child to complete the time-out, as well as because the child can earn extra credits for going to the time-out chair appropriately. The credit system also can be incredibly helpful when extended to the child's behavior at school, regardless of the school policy. It provides structure and accountability while simultaneously helping the parent convey an ongoing flow of appreciation.

Credit system: final cautions.

The Nurtured Heart credit system will fail if you relax the basic techniques. Appreciation is the foundation of The Nurtured Heart Approach, so **keep energizing success constantly.**

Failure also emerges if you look the other way when difficult behavior is occurring or when a rule is broken, or if you warn or remind. **The credit system is an excellent resource to help you NOT fall into the trap of looking the other way, warning or reminding, as well as an excellent resource to help you keep energizing success.**

Going back to Phase I and pumping it up with extensive acknowledgements can help you avoid using a credit system if that's your choice. But if you need to use the credit system, we need to outline a step-by-step method for your credit system that can be enacted with simplicity.

10 Good Reasons To Use a Credit System

1. It keeps boundaries and expectations clear.

2. It keeps the family on track.

3. It promotes consistency and routine.

4. It provides more opportunity for administering emotional nutrition to your child.

5. It is educational in that it teaches math skills and critical thinking.

6. It emphasizes finding "what's right with the picture" and creating more moments of success.

7. It can be expanded to include expected behavior while in school, at religious services, at family outings, or any other setting.

8. It encourages the child to take responsibility for positive (and negative) choices.

9. It is predictable and promotes NOT breaking the rules.

10. It is customized to meet the individual needs of each child.

It's A Lot Like Drip Irrigation

If you are at all familiar with farming or you live in a desert climate, you understand this concept. Drip irrigation is a complex series of tubes that is placed underground and delivers drips of water to plants in a continuous, gentle and steady stream. It is meant to water the root of the plant, where it is needed the most. The credit system is much like a drip irrigation system in that it is a steady stream of emotional nutrition administered in a strategic and organized way. It is meant to massage the heart of the child and optimize the parent-child connection.

To Summarize

At this point you realize that the credit system is an extension of the basic principles of appreciation and recognition and provides further opportunities to create success experiences for your child. We never give credits without a positive explanation of appreciation for what was accomplished. You can see that the credit system also gives the child a first-hand experience with an economy that will prepare her for the real-world economy in which we all live and function. You know that a slow and continuous drip irrigation system of reinforcing success gradually builds inner wealth in the child that will eventually have an ongoing life of its own. **You realize that not every child needs a credit system, but for those who do, it can be very helpful both at home and with the child's school issues.** You recognize that, for the credit system to work, you need to be committed to it. But most importantly, you know that you must consistently continue to energize success experiences on a daily basis.

The Next Step

If you have decided to proceed with a credit system, we will now help you design your own for use with your child.

Steps for Designing the Credit System
Step 1: Establish the rules.

Write out the list of rules.

The very first step in designing the credit system is to establish the rules. The rules must be in written form to ensure that both you and the child are aware of and committed to them. Remember the basketball game referee. He knows the rules, the player knows the rules, and both of them know that the other knows the rules. Have you ever seen the referee wait to start the game in order to go over the rules?

Rules that start with "no" are clear.

Rules should be as clear as possible. Rules are more clear and effective when they start with "no," such as no name-calling, no hitting, no arguing, no yelling, no back talk, no swearing, etc. Include essential rules that are unique to your family's needs but that are also respected in society. (Positive rules are discussed later in this section.)

Positive Rules are confusing because they blur the lines.

Out of the mouths of babes...

Co-author Lisa Bravo tells the story of her son and a trip to a nearby restaurant. Her two children decided to ride their scooters, while Lisa and her husband walked. Lisa realized that there would be areas where traffic would be heavy and she wanted the children to understand how important it would be NOT to ride ahead or be inattentive in any way. They had made the trip many times and they knew what to expect.

Out of the mouths of babes – Continued

Although Lisa tried to resist the urge to instruct them about being safe, she began to remind them by saying, "Okay you guys, remember what the rules are…." Her son interrupted her in a swift but respectful way and said, "Mommm…." Lisa answered, "You are right, I don't need to tell you. You are both very wise." With that her son gave her a kiss on the cheek and got on his scooter. The family had a peaceful walk, and everyone followed the rules…even though they were NOT recited prior to the trip.

What a relief! Everyone knows the rules, so we do not have to give them our energy anymore. All we have to focus on is creating successes, building relationships and giving a simple reset if a line is crossed!

Sample Rules List

Examples:	**My Family Rules:**
No Hitting	1. _____
No Lying	2. _____
No Stealing	3. _____
No Talking Back	4. _____
No Arguing	5. _____

Note: Writing them down is yet another way to commit to the rules.

Include only rules that you can monitor/evaluate.

It is vital to have rules that are within *your* ability to monitor and evaluate directly or indirectly. As in the courts, hearsay evidence is not fair or acceptable. Eliminate tattling altogether by making a 'No tattling' rule in your family. Encourage children to take responsibility for their own behavior. Empower them to find solutions to their dilemmas and exercise their healthy power. Applaud them for good choices when the problems are not happening.

Praise of Rules Not Broken Makes The Best Possible Warning

Remember: By applauding the child for NOT breaking the rules, you are reminding her, without feeding negativity, that the rules exist.

Nobody Likes a Hall Monitor

We all have them in our lives: the people who are more concerned about what **you** are or are not doing, instead of getting **their** job done. These are the incessant tattletales. When children are reinforced for tattling behavior, they come to learn that this is how they get adult relationship. They don't learn that when they grow up this type of interaction is not valued and can be downright annoying.

Oftentimes children tattletale because they feel powerless or intimidated. As parents, we can help children live within their own power by focusing on what they are doing well in the moment and not giving our attention or focus to what others are not doing. One great exception is that Nurtured Heart kids often turn tattling to a positive by telling about *good* things the other is doing!

What To Do About Name Calling

When Lisa Bravo's children were five and three, she hadn't yet learned the Nurtured Heart Approach. Her son went through a period when he would tease his younger sister and call her "stupid." Her intense son relished all that happened around him while this scenario ensued. His sister would run to mom to rescue her from her relentless brother. As his favorite 'toys,' his parents would get involved. He would have a traditional time-out, followed by a traditional lecture about how to treat his sister with kindness. It seemed to work initially, but the scenario kept occurring on a pretty consistent basis.

What To Do About Name Calling – Continued

Once she discovered The Nurtured Heart Approach, Lisa found a solution, not in changing her son's behavior, but in empowering her daughter. When Danielle ran to her mother to announce her dismay, instead of feeding the typical cycle, Lisa did something different. She began to actively recognize Danielle for handling her strong feelings and frustration. When Danielle tearfully stated that her brother called her "stupid," Lisa would ask, "Danielle, are you stupid?" Danielle would dig in her heels and with all the determination she could muster, say "NO!" Lisa said, "I see you not being stupid, I see you not giving away your power." Danielle quickly learned that she had the power to respond any way she chose. She then could be heard saying to her teasing brother, "I am not falling for that!" or "You're not getting MY power!" and walking away triumphantly. Eventually Christopher learned that there was nothing to be gained in teasing his sister.

Include "gimmie" rules.

Be sure to include some rules that are "gimmies," rules that your child might never break or are achievable on a consistent basis but are nonetheless important rules. Use of "gimmie" rules sets up opportunities for positive recognition of success and allows liberal awarding of credits. Some examples of "gimmie rules" might be: Going to school, wearing a seatbelt in the car, washing hands before dinner, getting dressed independently, spending time with siblings, bringing home homework, etc. Notice that these examples are very doable, and most children accomplish them consistently. "Gimme rules" are designed to create and energize success around the child.

Decide the number of credits you will award for each unbroken rule.

Decide how many credit points you will award for each of the rules when they are not broken. Using 10 or multiples of 10 is often convenient for rapid calculation. Using a standard number of credits for every rule does not tax your memory or that of your child. You can merely double the number of awarded points, if you wish, as a way to prioritize certain rules.

How is this different from Behavior Management Systems?

The problem with many credit systems is that they become too focused on where the child has failed throughout the day. In The Nurtured Heart Approach, we would rather tune into the times during the day when the child is NOT breaking the rules.

Step 2: Formalize a list of positive, desirable behaviors and qualities for which the child can earn bonus credits.

Write a list of Positive Choices/Bonus Credits.

These are desirable or sought-after positive behaviors and qualities that you want to encourage in your child. This list is similar to positive rules and might contain behaviors such as being polite and respectful, doing things when asked, being helpful, showing good manners, playing cooperatively, taking 'no' for an answer, etc. As with the other rules, make a list of these positive behaviors and qualities because the items will be tracked and credited, giving you the opportunity to reward via bonuses the behaviors you want to encourage.

Decide the number of bonus credits you will award.

Decide how many bonus credits each positive behavior will earn. Keep it simple and easy to calculate: for example, you might give 10 credits for each positive behavior.

About Bonus Credits

Bonus credits give you the power to create even more successes around your child. The purpose is to pump up the volume on the behaviors you want to see displayed more. Give bonus credits for holding it together during a difficult time of day; for being respectful and thoughtful even when upset; for remembering to do chores without complaining; or for appropriate handling of a problem at school.

The bonus credits you award for these behaviors might be:

- additional credits

- double credits for good choices that ultimately lead to good outcomes

- special "golden bonus credits" to be spent on a special event or activity

About Partial Credits

Remember Shamu and the toll taker? Partial credits are an effective way to give positive reinforcement for choices and behaviors that are just emerging and that you want to see grow. Giving partial credit is a way to say "I see that you are making an effort and I want to give you credit for that." Some common examples: when your child does only a portion of her chores, or stops herself from arguing, or goes most of the day without using bad words, or gets most of her homework done. **This system is really about deepening your child's attunement to positivity.** Here's how it might sound: "I see you've gotten some of your chores done. I appreciate that and I'm giving you partial credit." Or "Most of the day you didn't argue. That is really a nice change so I am giving you most of your 'no arguing' credits."

Step 3: Devise a list of chores and responsibilities for which you will award bonus credits.

Write out this "Chores and Responsibilities" list.

The chores and responsibilities need to be appropriate for your child's age and ability level.

Chore (noun): A minor duty or task.	**Responsibility** (noun): On one's own initiative or authority.

Chores include anything that can be done around home or the neighborhood.

Chores can include anything from simple to complex household or neighborly tasks that contribute to life on the home front. For example, raking leaves, doing the dishes, folding towels, etc.

Responsibilities include activities essential to the well-being of the child.

Responsibilities are those daily incidental aspects of life that are essential to the well-being of the child and the family. Examples include doing one's homework and turning it in, getting ready for school or bed on time, putting one's dirty clothes in the hamper, good personal hygiene, feeding the family pet, etc.

Remember, the simpler, the better, especially for younger children. A credit system may be overkill for smaller children. Typically, we don't recommend a credit system for children under age 5; however, some parents have reported doing it with some success. Chores for younger children should be simple, short tasks. For example, helping set the table, putting on their shoes, filling the dog's water bowl. Responsibilities may include brushing teeth (with assistance), helping put toys away, and toileting activities.

Take a moment to jot down the chores and responsibilities you desire for your child/children. Challenge yourself to make them reasonable and age appropriate (remember Shamu and the toll taker).

Chores
_____
_____
_____
_____
_____

Responsibilities
_____
_____
_____
_____
_____
_____

Decide the number of credits you will award for chores/responsibilities.

Chores and responsibilities vary as to level of difficulty, time and effort. Therefore, it is wise to use different credit values for these. For example, 'making the bed' might earn 20 credits, while 'having a good day at school' might earn 100.

You might also exercise the option of assigning credits spontaneously when something unusually good happens. For example, if your child argues frequently, then the first time you see him control that behavior (i.e., showing responsibility), you might give a spontaneous bonus – perhaps 100 credits or more because for the first time he has shown exceptional restraint, and that is a time to notice and reward it in a big fashion. You can include this possibility on your list by using an asterisk and stating that you will spontaneously award credits for particularly outstanding effort. In that way, you will be giving a "bonus" bonus. Partial credits also can be used to reward improvements toward the desired chore or responsibility. For example, if on a given day the child *reduces significantly* the number of arguments, he can be rewarded with a partial credit.

For non-readers, use appropriate symbols, such as stars, smiley faces, and so on, rather than number values for credits.

While some children are able to understand a number system and others may even be able to count by tens or hundreds, some children might not. Use what is appropriate for your child – whatever you need to make the awards concrete and understandable for your child.

On-The-Spot Credits

One way to really turn up the volume on your child's newfound success is to give on-the-spot credits. These are in-the-moment broadcasts or celebrations of a job well done or a moment well handled. You may wish to deliver these credits with a lot of pomp and circumstance. It's meant to be a "stop everything" moment in which you sing the praises of your child.

Credits, when delivered in this way, provide irrefutable evidence of your child's success, within the context of a first-hand experience.

Create successes that might not otherwise exist...a short story.

Lisa Bravo tells the story of her oldest child who often tried to get out of doing chores on Saturday morning. If he did do them, it was certainly half-heartedly, with a lot of foot dragging and whining. She tried to be proactive, make it fun, be positive, but it always turned out to be an exhausting endeavor. One day after she had started The Nurtured Heart Approach, she came upon a wonderful solution. She began the routine like any other Saturday, posting chores on the refrigerator wipe board. She summoned her two children.

As usual, Christopher began his mantra about how he hated doing chores. Lisa calmly waited and announced that "today is a double bonus day." She explained that we never know if it is going to be a "double bonus day" or not. She told Christopher, "It's up to you if you want to do your chores. I am not going to make you, but just know it's a double bonus day. And if you don't, as usual there will be a consequence." Although he was interested, he was not interested enough to do his chores. When his sister finished her chores, Lisa made a big production out of her accomplishment and gave her a $5 gift card to the toy store for "double bonus day."

The next week, Christopher got up early and finished all of his chores without even being asked. With Shamu in mind, Lisa actively recognized

...a short story – Continued

him for HIS accomplishment and gave him his gift card. From then on, chore day was no longer a problem. Lisa gave double bonuses like afternoon ice cream sundaes (expensive at 500 credits!) or movie nights. She kept the children guessing by changing prices and privileges often. Now, when Christopher is tempted to complain about a chore, he stops himself and says (sometimes audibly), "Well, I'm just gonna do them – you never know if it is a double bonus day!"

Step 4: Combine these three lists (rules, behaviors and chores/responsibilities) on one large page entitled "Ways to Earn Credits."

"Ways to Earn Credits" is the first of two essential categories of the credit system. Make sure they are in list form and are written clearly and concisely. The combination of credits and bonuses earned for **rules not broken,** for **positive behaviors** and for **efforts applied to chores and responsibilities** becomes earned credits.

Earned credits are used to purchase privileges.

Earned credits are NOT for things. They are for *privileges* only. Keep this in mind when making up all your lists.

Earned credits are NEVER taken away – they are only spent.

Credits that are earned are never taken away. In the case of lack of cooperation or for a particularly bad infraction, credits can be frozen (i.e., they cannot be spent for privileges), but they are not taken away or subtracted under The Nurtured Heart Approach. Remember, you are not a judge levying a fine, so what has been earned is earned and it remains in the "bank" for the child.

Ways To Earn

Add your own ways to earn credits. It is important to include your child in helping you come up with ways to earn so that they feel invested in the system. In essence, however, this list will simply restate the rules, behaviors, and chores/responsibilities you have already defined.

_____

_____

_____

_____

_____

_____

_____

_____

_____

_____

_____

_____

_____

_____

Step 5: Devise a list of privileges: Ways To Spend Credits.

This is a list of *specified privileges* you find acceptable for your child to work for or earn through constructive behavior. Make sure that terms and limits are clearly stated. Examples may include:

- going to the movies

- watching acceptable TV programs (for a specified period of time such as 30 minutes, with a 2 hour max – or whatever fits your family max)

- time on the computer (such as 30 minutes with a two-hour max)

- a meal at a fast-food restaurant

- one-half hour of skateboarding time (with a two-hour max)

- sleeping over at a friend's home (4 times a year max)

- special one-on-one time with a parent (1 hour)

You can get as creative as you wish, such as "buying maid service for 15 minutes." Individualize it to the needs of your child at a given age as well as to your needs and the needs of your family. **Remember, you get to decide what the terms, limits, and costs are!**

Ways To Spend

- Watching TV

- Computer time

- Lunch at a favorite restaurant

- Time at the park

- Video game time

- Extra outside time

- Sleepover at a friend's house

- Sleepover at your house

- "All About Me" time where your child picks from a list of activities to include a favorite meal, game, activity, etc.

- Bubble bath

- "My Pick" dinner night

- "My Pick" movie night

- Extended bedtime

- Trip to the library after school

- Grab Bag (can be filled with coupons for fast food, treats, $1 store items, etc.)

Bigger Ticket Items Might Include:

- A trip to the zoo

- A video game marathon

- A trip to the water park

- Trying a new sport as a family (such as ice skating, skiing, boating, volleyball, etc.)

- Trying a new restaurant as a family

- Tickets to a local sporting event, concert or other activity

- Picnic Day at the park or beach

- "Maid Service" for the day (at your discretion)

For Teens:

- Using the family vehicle

- Gas money

- Extended curfew

- Movie night with friends

- Time at the mall

Everything in life is really a privilege.

Real life credit systems are encompassing – we must pay for everything. Ask yourself, are we really doing a child a disservice if we charge them for everything? Therefore, as you make up the list of privileges, remember that everything in life is really a privilege, not a right. That includes things that the child might believe she is entitled to, such as maid service, chauffeur service, laundry services, etc. These are all things that have a cost for us. Remembering this helps you select the privileges to go on the list. **Ultimately, it is your decision what goes on the list.**

Tools For Organizing Your Credit System

These tried-and-true tools have been used by many families.

- Hang a wipe board in a central location. Use it to communicate daily chores or words of encouragement and inspiration.

- Create a daily note to be signed by teachers for completed homework, expected behaviors, etc., at school for which your child earns points at home. (More on this later.)

- Make *Nurtured Heart* currency (with each child's picture on it) as ways to earn credits, and/or make *Nurtured Heart* checkbooks as ways to track and spend credits.

Think of some other examples that will work for your family. Consider how your family processes information. Some need to have it written down in the form of charts, and some prefer it to be less formal and just verbally communicated. Choose the style that works best for you and your family. You may use the sample chart on the following page.

Ways to Earn:

_____

_____

_____

_____

_____

_____

_____

_____

_____

_____

_____

_____

Ways to Spend:

_____

_____

_____

_____

_____

_____

_____

_____

_____

_____

_____

_____

Be Creative

Be as creative as you need to be. For example, some television will be off limits. Other television that your child likes but you do not will be available at a higher price. You can encourage educational TV by making it both more available and less costly, as there truly is some excellent programming available these days. It is also okay to give bonus credits when the child demonstrates good management of the spending system or is honest about it when a parent makes a mistake. **Remember Shamu and the art of creating success that would otherwise not exist. Remember the toll taker and the way we choose to see things.**

Decide on the costs for each of the privileges.

Determine how many credits you want to charge for each privilege on the list and make sure the costs are clearly stated. Charge according to what you would like to encourage or discourage in your child. For example, watching educational television for a half hour might cost less than watching a program of the child's choice for a half hour. Figure the potential to earn between 200 and 500 credits per day for most children over six, with a more basic accounting system for younger children (such as 20 – 50 stars, tokens, etc). Similarly to the older child, the younger child pays for privileges with stars, tokens, etc. Costs/charges should be determined based on the age of the child as well as the child's counting ability. Individualize this as much you need.

Estimate how many credits your child may typically earn and how much time your child normally needs to use for privileges each day.

The total cost of your child's average daily privileges (i.e., the number of credits charged for a given activity) should add up to approximately 50 to 75 percent of the total daily credits that are potentially earned. This allows your child to continue usual activities by exerting a reasonable amount of effort and provides incentive to work and save for bigger, less frequent privileges, like going to a movie or getting to do something special.

Charges can be revised as needed.

Keep in mind that you can revise costs/charges as needed. You might discover that you have overcharged or undercharged initially. You might also want to revise costs as the needs of the child change. Also, for a more intense child, values can be recalculated so as to produce more leverage by making privileges increasingly expensive. We recommend, however, that you start out with the general accounting described above.

Write out your "Ways to Spend Credits" list that includes specified charges.

Write out this list. Make sure costs are specific. Place the list next to the Ways to Earn Credits list for easy reference.

Ways To Make It Pop!

There are many creative ways to spend credits. Challenge yourself to go beyond stickers and smiley faces. If you take a few extra minutes to personalize it for your family, they will be more invested in the system. For older children, have them make suggestions about what they want as privileges.

Cool Ideas:

Treasure Hunt – Kids earn credits toward a family treasure hunt created by the parents. It can be elaborate or simple. You can use commonly found items or favorite toys.

Bravo Bucks – This is merely a catchy term, or theme, for credits. "Bravo Bucks" are ways to spend credits.

Monopoly $ – A large family we know of had an innovative way to keep track of whose money was whose. The mother photocopied her children's faces on different denominations of "money" and handed them out accordingly. Money did not get mixed up anymore!

A Nurtured Heart Checkbook – One family printed credit system checks on the computer. Each child had their own checkbook and kept track of their balance, credits, etc. When they wanted to spend credits, they did so by writing a check (a VERY creative way to teach everyday math).

The Mystery Bag – The child can choose from the mystery bag when chores are partially completed to recognize her positive attitude, hard work, staying on task, etc. The bag contains extra credit coupons or other surprises. The idea is to keep it light and keep it fun.

Think of some other ways to make it POP! Take a few minutes to jot them down in THIS moment when your thoughts are generating.

_____

_____

_____

_____

_____

_____

_____

Step 6: Set up a daily review time with your child.

Decide upon a convenient daily review time with your child lasting 5 to 10 minutes maximum. After the evening meal is often a good time.

The Daily Review – What it is…and what it isn't.

The daily review is a time to celebrate the successes of the day. It should be done consistently and daily. It IS a time to discuss what went well, within the structure of the credit system. It is an opportunity to convey relationship, love and connection and to build on the successes of that day. It IS NOT a time to give the sermon about what went wrong, what they could have done better, might have accomplished, should have tried, did not do, etc. After a difficult day, it can be very tempting to go down this road. Remember, even a drop of negativity is still negativity and is still gas on the very fire that you are trying to put out. The purpose of the daily review is to deliver yet another blast of irrefutable evidence that your child's new portfolio of success is the only portfolio that you are interested in.

During the daily review, tally the credits earned and subtract the privileges purchased by the child.

This can be done on a piece of paper or you may want to keep a journal, log, calendar, or Nurtured Heart Approach checkbook with the child to help him recognize his progress as well as for bookkeeping purposes. Some parents use a chalkboard or dry marker board in a central location, which can be erased when it is filled up. Use of these recording methods also allows you to give credits spontaneously throughout the day when you see the positive behaviors occurring. Your memory will not be taxed if you write them down immediately. Remember also that the child gets to accumulate the credits that are left over from a given day to be put in her "bank" for use at a later time, such as the weekend or a special privilege or trip for which she is saving. Using a written record will assist with that type of bookkeeping also.

Basically, the daily accounting involves daily credits earned, minus daily credits spent or planned to be spent by the child later that night. As a family, you decide what credits can be spent. For example, an extra 15 minutes at bedtime can be spent tonight, whereas a movie night has to wait for the weekend to be redeemed.

Although many children love to do the accounting themselves, it is up to you to award the credits. This better defines you as "in charge" of the credit system and gives you more power in the form of authority, convenience and neutrality. Instead of being arbitrary, your decisions are based on the rules and stipulations of the credit system. Later on, however, you can expand the system to respond to the child's increasing degrees of accurate self-evaluation and self-recognition.

Physical markers of success can be awarded during the daily review.

Often it is easier and more convenient to use some customized form of currency as physical markers of credit, even with older children. Many families choose to use poker chips, play money or homemade tokens or tickets. This works well in families using the system with more than one child. By using some sort of marker, the accounting takes care of itself.

Be generous with the credits and give bonus points when they are earned.

Be generous with credits and bonus points, including rewarding your child if he participates appropriately during the daily review. The object is to help the child feel wealthy. The wealth is always earned through successful behavior.

If the child is feeling wealthy with his credits, chances are he is well on his way to feeling great about who he is. Our experience bears out that, as children start feeling great about who they are, they manifest it by living their lives in more productive ways.

Get Unplugged!

One way to continue to connect in lasting and positive ways is to have one night a week where you get unplugged. The idea is to turn off the TV, radios, CD players, I-Pods, video games, computers, cell phones, etc. The kids can help with meal planning. Older children can make meals on their own! This is a night to dust off those board games, cards, or art projects, and experience relationship, connection, and fun!

Cost-Free Privileges

Be sure to continue creating success every day. One way to keep the kids in the game is to offer creative family activities a couple of times a week. They are cost-free and designed to improve family time. They can be planned in addition to credit system privileges. Here are some ideas:

- Family game night

- Movie night

- Rock, paper, scissors tournament to decide who gets what chore, who gets to take the first shower, who wins the negotiation.

During the review, be neutral and objective.

Be matter-of-fact with your child. Be specific about the positives you see. Do **not** lecture about or discuss any failures. Be a supportive consultant, relaying positives, credits earned and credits spent, rather than a judge and jury deciding your child's privilege fate. Your child ultimately will feel that you and the world are more fair, consistent and predictable, a welcome anchor to a child who has previously been confused about how she fits into the big picture.

A Word on Community Service

For an older child or adolescent who has committed an infraction that you deem is major and should require a stiffer penalty than a time-out, you can add an additional fine in the form of community service. For example, on the rules list, you might use a symbol, such as an asterisk, to designate which rules are considered major rules that, when violated, will require community service in addition to a time-out. The rules of "No Hitting," "No Destroying Things," or "No Violating Curfew" might fall in this category.

When one of these starred rules is broken, the child will automatically understand that a community service is added to the time-out. Both the length and type of community service are at the discretion of the parent. You might also consider allowing your child to make suggestions about what he should do for community service. The more invested he is in the process, the more likely he is to do his service.

Examples of Community Service

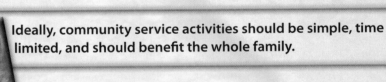

For Older Children:

- Emptying the garbage
- Taking the dog for a walk
- Cleaning the kitchen
- Straightening up the family room
- Vacuuming
- Dusting
- Washing the family car
- Cleaning up the yard
- Cleaning the garage

For Younger Children:

- Wiping off the table
- Picking up the family room
- Helping load the dishwasher
- Picking the weeds
- Wiping the windows
- Wiping down the sink
- Picking up loose trash outside
- Straightening the toy area
- Stacking picture books

Ideally, community service activities should be simple, time limited, and should benefit the whole family.

Spending on privileges will be on hold until both the time-out and the community service are completed. The child would still earn credits for appropriate behaviors eligible for credits, even if completion of the community service is delayed. Spending of credits, however, is always frozen until the child chooses to finish the time-out and the community service, unless other arrangements have been made. Community service can be anything that helps the home, the school community, the church community, the neighborhood or any other creative contribution to others.

Eventually, they begin to do their community service ahead of time.

We have found that when children become accustomed to this approach, and they experience success after success, they intrinsically want to do the right thing. At the times they do make a poor choice, they are much more likely to take responsibility immediately and make another choice in the right direction. They increasingly act with integrity.

The Wrap Up

The credit system works like this:

1. When your child follows a rule, shows an example of good behavior, or performs a chore or responsibility, she will be entitled to earn the corresponding credits.

2. She then spends the credits on any of the designated privileges.

    - Remember that credits and charges need to be clearly defined and that once a credit is earned, it is NEVER taken away.

    - Remember to give credits generously to help the child feel wealthy, as well as to award bonus credits and partial credits when appropriate.

    - Community service can be added to the time-out consequence.

    - Credits are frozen and may not be used until time-outs and community service have been served.

    - Be consistent in conducting the daily review with your child. This is very important because it helps the child see her progress.

    - Remember: the heart of the system is to create and cultivate a healing level of successes over an extended period of time.

The Next Step

We are now ready to move on to the important procedure of how to present the credit system to the child.

How to Present the Credit System to the Child

Having experienced the many acknowledgements and recognitions and the strong flow of emotional nutrition you are providing, your child should by now be responding, at least somewhat, to those positive experiences. You might have noticed that he has an increased excitement and interest in family life as evidenced by progress in the areas of respect, responsibilities, following the rules, and other such improvements. This is a signal that it is time to present the credit system and to involve your child in this powerful means of magnifying time-ins for his good behaviors. Below are some strategies for presenting the credit system, as well as how to proceed if your child initially rejects your version of it.

Always present the credit system in a positive way.

For example, you might say, *"Hey, look how well it went last week. I have really seen you use more effort lately in following the rules and making positive choices. When things weren't going well, I wasn't so willing to help you get the privileges you wanted. Now that things are so much better, I'd actually like to be of assistance. So here's the idea I have. I think you deserve to earn credit every day for the efforts you've been making. I have come up with a way you can earn privileges based on your good efforts. Here is what I have in mind…."*

Explain the mechanics of the system.

Explain how the Rules list, the Positive Behaviors list and the Chores and Responsibilities list are incorporated into the Ways to Earn Credits list. Then explain the Ways to Spend Credits list, along with the method you have chosen to use as a marker. After you feel assured the child understands the mechanics, explain the daily review process.

Include the child in the process of developing rules, privileges and credits.

When explaining the various lists, allow the child's input about rules, privileges and credits. For example, you might say, *"You know all the rules you didn't break, because I have been telling you that I noticed. I have written down some of those rules but I might have missed some. Can you think of other rules that could be on the list that you can get credits for not breaking?"*

Then say, *"Here are some bonuses for positive choices that I have in mind…can you think of any others?"*

Then say, *"Here are some chores and responsibilities I have I mind…can you think of any others?"*

What to Do if the Child Resists

Most kids will be drawn to the possibilities of earning and spending in addition to the compelling nature of being appreciated. They can see around the corner and sense that this will work out just fine. Yet for others, this new sense of greatness that we are trying to instill has not fully blossomed. The old ways of negative thinking might still be looming, and the fact that they have always had free access to these privileges can exacerbate their negative reaction.

It is possible that your child will question all this and still be willing to move forward. But it's also possible that your child will take a stance of rejecting this proposal.

Please do not fall into the trap of a power struggle – the credit system does not have to flow right away. There are alternative ways to get it off the ground if you want it to happen. For example, try something like: *"Because last week went so well, I want to give you a bonus. If you start up (this system) by accepting it despite your concerns, I will give you an additional bonus."*

If the child still rejects the idea, however, here's what we recommend you do and say: *"It's okay for you to not want to do this; I understand and you have my permission to not want to do it. What you need to know, however, is that I have decided this makes sense. I very much want to help you get the privileges you have been asking for.*

"First of all, I'm going to set aside a bonus for last week. The positive changes I've seen in you have made me so happy. I'll continue to let you know how much I appreciate your positive choices, and I'm going to also start giving you credits when I see those choices happening. You'll be able to spend those on privileges. BUT the only thing you need to know is that, as much as I want you to have your privileges now that things are better, the only way they are available is if you choose to get them with your credits. So let me know if and when you decide you want to use them."

The worst-case scenario is that the child will storm off and refuse to do the credit system. He might say, "I'm not going to do your stupid credit system!" KEEP YOUR COOL! Don't fret and fuss over it. In our experience, it is typically not that long before the child comes back and says, "Okay, I will give it a try." Remember to value that choice and be appreciative. For example, *"Thanks for reconsidering; I know it's a big decision. I appreciate the thought you have put into making your decision."* Keep in mind that this *is* a big and important decision for your child. The child is not relenting because you grounded him, but he came to realize he grounded himself!

Our challenging children seem to prosper from this kind of quiet power – this mulling it over and thinking it through time – as well as the quiet power they experience when we take stands such as the one noted above. They will need their own internal version of quiet power throughout life as they learn to handle their greater level of personal intensity.

Tip: Start off by giving a bonus (a lump sum) …for doing a great job in the recent past. This will help to get the ball rolling.

So, was I supposed to take things away?

Many parents who are accustomed to traditional parenting approaches often ask this question. It may be confusing to have your child "pay for" things she already does each day. Does this mean you should take away everything and then let her "buy it" back? NO, NO, NO! You do not need to literally empty out your child's room, removing TVs, CDs, etc. It simply means that, if you decide to make these activities a privilege, you will now be charging for their usage. Your child will be gaining a first-hand experience of a REAL economy. **Remember, these things are privileges, NOT rights.**

For the most defiant child, wait out the resistance in your most neutral manner. Occasionally let the child know that his privileges are available only through credits and he has credits accumulated to spend whenever he is ready. **Continuing to give recognition and credit in the meantime is the key.** Continue pulling your child in a positive direction despite his understandable attempts to keep things the way they used to be.

Continue to give generous verbal recognition.

Don't let ANYTHING stop you from super-energizing success. This is the mindset we recommend always. **Do not allow yourself to be derailed at this juncture. Hold your ground by keeping the flow of recognition high.**

Remember: Challenging kids seem to prosper from mastering their personal intensity by learning how to use their "quiet power" to arrive at a successful decision.

Lowering The Rope

Co-author Lisa Bravo relays the following story to illustrate the point: *My 10-year-old son had been doing consistently well on the credit system. Part of his program included a daily note, signed by his teachers that described his daily behavior and school performance. If he did not bring it home daily, or he failed to complete his homework assignments from the night before, the consequence was that "the store was closed" and he would not be able to spend his credits after school to go out and play. He was pretty consistent about bringing the note home with only a few blips on the screen every now and then.*

It was Halloween morning, a Tuesday, and my son began his day like any other, getting himself ready for school. He had his pirate costume laid out in the living room for two days in anticipation of the big event. I suppressed the urge to remind him about making sure he had everything he needed for school and to bring his note home. He was well aware that there would be no exceptions even though it was Halloween. Around 10:00 a.m., I received a voicemail from my calm but noticeably stressed-out son stating, "Hi Mom, I forgot my workbook at home, so I know I have my consequence. That means I can't go trick-or-treating tonight. I really want to go, but I know I have a consequence." With that he hung up. Everything in me wanted to change my mind, give in to him, not be consistent, and essentially look the other way.

Close to tears, I called my husband, knowing it was going to be a hard lesson and wondering if we were being too strict about the rule, but it had been going so well and I did not want to jeopardize all the progress we had made. To think that he called me from school to tell on himself! That never would have happened a year ago. My husband, the logical one, said, "A consequence is a consequence, no matter what day it is. He can help pass out candy with me if he can hold it together." In my heart I knew it was the right thing to do, but I felt sad for my little boy.

When he got home from school, my son again told me he forgot to bring his homework to school. In a last desperate measure, he asked if he could go trick-or-treating. When I said no, he burst into tears and PUT HIMSELF IN TIME-OUT in his room.

Lowering The Rope – Continued

Within about 15 minutes, he had calmed down and stopped crying. He came out of his room and calmly and respectfully told me he had found a solution: he wanted to use his saved credits to buy a "Get Out of Jail Free" privilege. This was worked into the credit system at its inception because he previously had so many red days at school. (At his school, the discipline system was delineated by a color system of green for go, yellow for caution, and red for trouble. If the child got a "red day," it meant no recess, a trip to the principal, and a note or phone call home to the parent.) Just like Shamu's trainers had done, we made it a part of his credit system as a way to lower the rope. He could use the "Get Out of Jail Free Card" to forego one consequence per school year. It was only available once a school year and was not applicable for "big deal rules" like fighting at school, swearing, or hurting others. Also, initiating the use of the card had to be done by him. VOILA! He had found a way to solve the problem in a calm and productive manner!

There were many choices my son could have made throughout the day, such as falling apart at school and having a rotten day. He also chose to be respectful and stayed in control when it was clear I was not going to cave in. In NOT losing his cool, he was being successful. Because of his accumulated inner wealth, he was able to assess the situation and rely on his own problem-solving abilities to get to the other side. Through the credit system, we created a structure built on success and healthy problem-solving. He was able to experience profound success within the context of a first-hand experience. A win/win situation for all involved.

Don't Dangle Carrots!

Avoid the power struggle when presenting the credit system to the child. Be mindful of not accidentally giving relationship through negativity.

Let your child know that he will not be able to obtain privileges except by purchasing them with his earned credits.

That is what the system is for – to help him get his privileges. It is up to you and the other adults supporting the credit system start-up NOT to allow any privilege unless it is acquired through the new system. The credit system is another tool that helps you support your child. Through your eagerness to help him get privileges he did not have access to when he was being difficult, he learns that you are there in a role of support, cheering him on as he reaches his goals.

Dealing With Resistance

Remain neutral…Ride it out…KNOW that it is temporary.

Always charge for privileges that have been enjoyed without permission.

If you discover that a privilege has been enjoyed without your permission, you must charge for it accordingly. Some parents tell their child in advance that the cost of privileges taken without permission will be doubled. Assure your child that, after a trial period, future changes to the credit system can be negotiated.

Always stay positive

Most children are convinced of the system's benefits within one or two weeks. Some children can see the beauty of it instantly. Hearing the words "These are the credits you earned for your efforts today" is very fulfilling for them. The daily process helps them feel more confident in their ability to obtain a fair amount of privileges while accepting that they will be paying their own way now. For most children, it soon becomes a symphony of fun, mastery and pride in accomplishment.

For the child who has enjoyed negative control, a shift begins toward appreciating the greater benefits of positive control. With such a child, remind them, "It's up to you to decide what you will put your effort into and how you will spend the credits you've earned. I will make sure you get credit for the efforts you make." You are then out of the **role of being critical** and into a more powerful **role of support.**

You make the decision about when the child is allowed to go off the system.

If the child asks to go off the system and you believe staying with it will continue to benefit him, continue to assert that this is simply the only alternative through which privileges can be acquired. Calmly and neutrally state the impossibility of obtaining privileges other than through the credit system.

So, how long do we need to stay on a credit system?

This is completely up to you. Consider what your goals are for your child and your relationship with your child. Remember, the credit system is an effective tool in terms of keeping everyone on track while fanning the flames of success. Research shows that bad habits take an average of six weeks to break. When forming a new habit, it takes the same amount of time. Commit to six weeks and then reassess. Our experience shows that staying with this for the long run is the way to go. Remember, we adults are all on our own credit system for the long run.

Expect that your child may test the strength of this new role and system.

In our experience, children who challenge the system gain a great deal of benefit from the process. If your child tests the system, remain firm and merely repeat that the *only* way to obtain privileges is through the system. **Do not energize by arguing or lecturing, etc.** Merely stay the course. Continue to **energize success** and **give a consequence** when a rule is broken. What is important is your firmness, consistency and willingness to continue with the positives.

The Slippery Slope

ESPECIALLY when things are going well, it is easy to go back to reminders, looking the other way, etc. It is, indeed, a slippery slope. Keep this in mind as you continue down the road of transformation.

What It Looks Like When the Credit System is Working for Your Family

A lot of families find that the credit system keeps them on track. Some families report that it is way too tempting to revert to old habits without the structure of the credit system. Other families that are large in size or very busy say it helps them keep their priorities in order. When a caregiver or school is involved, the credit system is a way to promote a common language and keep the approach at the forefront. The credit system can be an important step in overhauling the culture of your family. That's the single biggest reason we recommend that people keep this going over a long period of time.

Still, for some families, this is just a way to change the pattern of negativity that has developed. The credit system is a way to keep the structure in place until its benefits become second nature. Just like a diet or exercise routine, if you stick to it faithfully, it will become part of your lifestyle, whether formally or informally.

Include siblings who are over five years of age in the credit system.

Most families do best when all the children in the family over the age of five are on the credit system. This prevents jealousy and any sense of preferential treatment among siblings. The system can easily be tailor-made for each child's needs and appropriate expectations. Or, you can choose to use one inclusive system when that is possible. Including siblings also provides them with recognition for their successes so that they, too, can begin to benefit and thrive at even greater levels. Consistent, positive acknowledgment of any child promotes a family atmosphere that is upbeat and prevents children from having to create involvement and connection for other than positive reasons.

> **With the credit system, EVERYONE wants to be in the game**

Keep in mind that the credit system works like a ***drip irrigation system*** to provide a steady flow of emotionally nutritious refueling. Through this process, you are building your child's sense of connection and comfort with experiencing success as well as a sense of mastery and accomplishment. You are further inspiring the child to his new sense of greatness.

The Nurtured Heart Kid

Co-author Lisa Bravo was in the toy store checkout line with her children when Danielle's insight taught her an amazing lesson. In line in front of them was a child three or four years old with his mother. He had picked up a candy bar from the rack and announced that he wanted it. As Lisa braced for the ensuing tantrum, his mother stopped writing out her check, knelt down and calmly said, "I need you to put it back. We are not going to buy that." She stood up and resumed making her purchase. The boy looked at the candy with longing eyes but slowly put it back. The mother picked him up, said something appreciative, gave him a hug, and left the store.

Unbeknownst to Lisa, Danielle was closely observing this whole exchange. She looked at Lisa with reverent eyes and said, "That boy is so lucky to be a Nurtured Heart kid." When asked what she meant, she said, "I could tell that boy really wanted the candy bar, but he used his strong power to do the right thing. He also wanted to respect his mom, so he listened to her. I could see how proud his mom was when she gave him that big hug." Awed by her daughter's insight, Lisa told Danielle how much she loved her and thanked her for sharing her wisdom. In that moment, Lisa was reminded of the beauty of seeing the world through a child's eyes.

A Word on Teamwork

To strengthen the approach and make it less likely for your child to manipulate things negatively to his advantage, it is best if all adults intervening or monitoring the child in your home are in clear agreement with the credit system. If agreement cannot be obtained, request that you alone handle the credit system and any consequences with the child for the time being until agreement can be reached. If there is another adult in the home who is interacting with your child in a way that is counter to your purposes and plan, try to do your best despite his or her influence. Once all the steps are in place and you have demonstrated their positive effects through changes in your child, you may be pleasantly surprised how this success impacts everyone around you, and you may find that cooperation can be achieved.

Please ALWAYS give acknowledgment and appreciation while giving credits!

Simply giving credits without the specific recognition of the accomplishments and the greatness involved defeats the purpose of the system – that is, to deepen and expand the child's awakening to his successfulness.

The Wrap Up

- You first need to explain the mechanics of the system – specifically how the system works.

- Include the child in the process of developing the rules, privileges and credits.

- Remember that the system usually works best when siblings over five years of age are included.

- Some children might resist the system, in which case you continue giving appreciation and recognition while at the same time (and in a neutral manner) informing the child that the only way to earn privileges is through the use of earned credits.

The Wrap Up – Continued

- You are alert to the fact that some children may violate the system but you should always charge for privileges that have been used without permission.

- Flexibility is important, and changes can be made in the system over time as needed.

- Be creative in ways to give credits and generous when giving them, even during the time when you are introducing the credit system to a resistant child.

- You make the decision about when the child is allowed to go off the system.

- You are aware that your child may test the strength of your role and the system, and if so, stay the course neutrally while giving consequences when any line is crossed and by continuing to give your energy to the positive behaviors you see.

- Teamwork is very important when a credit system is used.

The Next Step

If you want to extend the credit system to the school, you are now ready to learn how to do so.

CHAPTER 5

Phase IV:
Extending the Success to School

Now that you have the essential ingredients of The Nurtured Heart Approach – creating successes, refusing to energize negativity, and establishing clear limits and consequences – the chances are you might want to extend the successes you have achieved at home to your child's school experience.

Not every child who presents problems at home also has issues at school. But if this has been your experience, extending The Nurtured Heart Approach to the school system is often an important component of your child's overall success.

There are two main ways to propose implementation of The Nurtured Heart Approach in the classroom. You can use a direct approach if you feel that the teacher will be receptive to using the techniques that you have found to produce positive changes at home, and if you feel comfortable proposing these changes to the teacher directly. Simply explain to the teacher the essentials of the approach. Some parents also loan or give a copy of the Transforming the Difficult Child book to the teacher. Then describe to the teacher the tremendous successes you have had with your child. Solicit the teacher's cooperation by asking him to consider establishing the basics of the approach in your child's classroom. Offer to assist in any way you can to help the teacher understand and implement those basics.

If you experience hesitance or resistance from your child's teacher, a more indirect route may be advisable. This route requires, however, that you have established the credit system laid out in the previous chapter. Put simply, this would involve requesting that the teacher complete a daily checklist (explained in detail later in this chapter). Credits earned at school can be added to credit system totals at home.

Regardless of the route you choose based on your individual circumstances, we want you to walk away from this workbook feeling empowered and assured that the impact you have created at home can also translate to the child's school behavior. Our goal in this phase is to help you learn how to accomplish that.

Did you know that 50% of all teachers quit within the first three years?

Today's teachers are faced with greater demands and fewer resources. When implemented in the school system, The Nurtured Heart Approach has demonstrated increased teaching time, improved test scores, decreased behavior problems, decreased referrals for special education and mental health assessment, and increased teacher retention. If you would like more information about how to implement the Nurtured Heart Approach within the school, we urge you to read Notching Up the Nurtured Heart Approach: The New Inner Wealth Initiative for Educators by Howard Glasser and Melissa Lynn Block.

Did you know – Continued

This book focuses on the teacher's role in how to work with children, and particularly difficult children, in today's educational system. Educators can use this book to implement the Nurtured Heart Approach in their schools. It is an excellent resource for anyone in the educational system. (By the way, it also makes a wonderful teacher gift!)

The Teacher and the Difficult Child in the Classroom

The vast majority of teachers enter into the profession for all the right reasons. They have high regard for children, are concerned about them, and wish to do their best to impart wisdom and knowledge to the children in their charge. Unfortunately, however, many teachers are not trained to work with difficult children. They have learned methods of classroom management and discipline that work effectively with typical children most of the time. They do the best they can with the tools they have. But, as you have learned through parenting your own child, these conventional techniques wind up not working with a difficult child. In fact, conventional attempts to help difficult children typically make matters worse. Why is this? Again, it is because conventional teaching methods, like traditional parenting techniques, have the payoffs of energy and relationship in all the wrong places.

The conventional techniques usually have two other major shortcomings. They fail to energize and create successes with sufficient intensity, and they fail to set clear limits and clear consequences. You now know that in order to produce change it is essential that these elements be in place and used consistently on a daily basis in a powerful and transforming way.

A Precarious Position

This puts you in a precarious position. You have learned how to help your child therapeutically shift to successes, which in turn strengthens the child's positive orientation and ability to use self-control. The question becomes, "How do I get my new-found techniques for creating success across to a teacher who has been taught conventional methods of dealing with my difficult child?"

In the following pages, we will describe what we believe are reasonable steps to help resolve this dilemma. This intervention is designed to improve your child's performance dramatically regardless of whether or not the teacher knows The Nurtured Heart Approach. But first, we will present an incredibly important underlying construct that will help all this fall into place.

Someone is Watching

As we all know, many people have a deep and all-abiding connection with and faith in God. As part of that faith, many believe that God is watching them and everyone. They further believe that God can and will hold them accountable for their thoughts and actions, both good and bad. This belief helps many to develop the wherewithal to walk the straight and narrow and make positive rather than negative choices.

It is very unusual, on the other hand, for a young child to be guided in quite the same manner, even if the child is on a path of faith. Because children are in the process of developing, they do not yet possess the same deep, abiding and expansive commitment that adults do. We as parents have to temporarily represent God in the child's life. That is, we fulfill a similar role in that the child perceives us as all-seeing, all-knowing, all-wise, all-powerful and all-loving.

Think a moment about times you might have been in your child's classroom. When children know their parent is present and observing, often they are able to conjure up an extra measure of self-control and resiliency that might be absent or underutilized if mom or dad were not present. Somehow the knowledge of a parental presence enhances and benefits the child's abilities to perform at a higher level. It is nice to think that we are directly creating the improvements, but we are not. In actuality, it is the child's perception of being accountable to us that gives him the extra control and motivation.

It is the child's perception of being accountable to US (the parents) that gives her the extra measure of control and motivation.

Our job, then, is to create a new scenario in which our child benevolently perceives that we are in the back of the classroom, so to speak, without actually being there. Bringing about this perception further enhances our children's ability to function more successfully at school.

Our experience bears this out dramatically. We can indeed have a profound effect on our child's school performance by playing our "God-like" role. We do that by effectively extending the strategies that are already underway at home to the classroom. The methods that follow are geared to help develop the perception in that child that "God (in this case, the parent) is watching."

The Steps That Put It All Into Motion

The Methodology for the Elementary Age Child

Step 1: Create Your Checklist

First and foremost, it is critical to make this process as simple as possible, both for the child and for the teacher – to make it "doable" for everyone involved. This method should take the teacher no more than 30 seconds daily. The idea is to create a joint venture that no one can claim as unworkable. This is accomplished by providing simple checklists on cards or sheets of paper where, through observation, the teacher will make simple assessments of your child.

You will notice in the following sample that the checklist combines rules, goals and potential bonus areas that the parent and/or teacher feels are relevant for the particular child. The lists need to include "gimmie" items that both parent and teacher know will yield some level of success, along with rules and behaviors with which the child is currently struggling. The lists can be adjusted on an ongoing basis to include new relevant areas.

Here are possible rules and goals to consider for your child's checklist. It is always most beneficial if the teacher is willing to cooperate and provide input as to what items should be on your child's assessment. (Note: Because you will be using the checklist results to award credits and bonuses at home, the rules/goals should be consistent with your already established credit system there.)

Completing class work	Following directions
Good playground behavior	Good lunchroom behavior
No put-downs	No aggression
Good participation	No angry outbursts
No arguing	No teasing or distracting
Good attitude	Good self-control
Being respectful	Showing responsibility
Sharing or cooperating	Good problem-solving
Paying attention	Staying in seat when appropriate

Here is a sample checklist for the elementary-aged child. We've supplied you with two copies in case you decide to photocopy the page for your own use.

Elementary School Credit System

Name _____ Date _____ Teacher Initials _____

	Poor	Fair	Good	Very Good	Excellent
Paying attention	☐	☐	☐	☐	☐
Good attitude	☐	☐	☐	☐	☐
Following directions	☐	☐	☐	☐	☐
No bad words	☐	☐	☐	☐	☐
No aggression	☐	☐	☐	☐	☐

Comments _____

Elementary School Credit System

Name _____ Date _____ Teacher Initials _____

	Poor	Fair	Good	Very Good	Excellent
Paying attention	☐	☐	☐	☐	☐
Good attitude	☐	☐	☐	☐	☐
Following directions	☐	☐	☐	☐	☐
No bad words	☐	☐	☐	☐	☐
No aggression	☐	☐	☐	☐	☐

Comments _____

Note that the teacher merely checks one of five ratings (Poor, Fair, Good, Very Good, Excellent) that rates the child's behaviors for that date for that particular item on the list. (Some families with children who are extra sensitive to words use a 1-5 rating scale.) Whichever format you choose, make it as user-friendly as possible. **It is what you do with the completed assessment that works a little magic,** as you will soon see.

Step 2: Meet with the Teacher

Once you have created your checklist, arrange a meeting with the teacher. Keep the meeting as brief as possible and focus only on the plan. Avoid digressing into complaints, and keep it positive and moving along. Explain to the teacher that you have been using The Nurtured Heart Approach at home and you want to form a link between home and school to improve the child's behavior even more. You might want to take the time to succinctly explain the successes you are experiencing at home, and how the heightened recognition and clear limits have helped your child. You may also want to provide her with the basics of The Nurtured Heart Approach, which you will find in the pages just following. Assure the teacher that collaborating with you will make her job easier. Explain also that you plan to give your child credit, acknowledgment and accountability at home for his academic and behavioral efforts at school. (Note: "At home" acknowledgment and accountability will be explained later.)

Show the teacher a sample of the checklist. Ask for the teacher's input regarding areas in which she would like to see improvements in your child. Reassure the teacher that this process takes only a few seconds at the end of the day. Stress to the teacher the need to give positive marks for any aspects of that day that were NOT problems, as well as to give partial credit for problem areas where any degree of effort was made and the child has shown some improvement. One instance of poor choice or behavior does not seal the fate of a "bad" day. Emphasize that credit must be given for the part of the day that went well. Assure the teacher that this will make her job EASIER.

If you are not able to arrange a meeting, you can send a letter to the teacher that explains your goals and the teacher's role. Here is an example:

Sample Explanation Letter

Dear Ms. Smith,

The purpose of this letter is to request your assistance in helping Jeremy be more successful in school. We have been doing a credit system at home with much success, and I thought it would be helpful to extend it to his school day.

Enclosed you will find a daily note. I ask only that you observe him and rate his success on the behaviors listed, then sign it for Jeremy to bring home each day. Jeremy understands it is his responsibility to remember to give you the note each day and to bring it home each afternoon. If he forgets the note or has a "bump in the road" at school, he understands that he will have a consequence at home.

When you rate Jeremy, please give positive marks to the aspects of his day that were NOT problems. If there was some degree of effort or some improvement in a given category, please give him recognition for that with one of the mid-range scores. Please rate "Poor" if Jeremy has shown no improvement and/or if that particular category continues to be a significant problem.

I know that you are very busy and I tried to make the daily note very easy for you to complete. I appreciate your willingness to help Jeremy have a successful year. If you have any questions or concerns or additional items you would like to see on the checklist, please feel free to call me at (555) 555-5555.

Sincerely,

Mary Salinger

There are many options for customizing the checklist system for the teacher, the child and you. For example:

- For very young children, you can supply the teacher with a number of checklists at one time, and the teacher can put one in the child's backpack at the end of each day.

- You can decide in advance how frequently you need to have the teacher's feedback (i.e., daily, every other day, weekly) and on which day(s) you will need the child to take and bring home the checklist. Some parents find it makes sense to require that a *daily* checklist be brought home to keep your child in the habit of remembering the credit system while at school. Once decided, inform the teacher of this decision about frequency.

- You can have the child give you the note during the daily review or immediately after school and you can build in a reward for this in the credit system.

If you are organized in advance and have clearly articulated your purpose, most teachers will assist with this classroom accommodation with little hesitation. If, however, the teacher's cooperation is not forthcoming, consult the policy of your local school or district as to advocacy advice on classroom accommodation, and follow that policy.

Generally speaking, the more involved you are as a parent, the more open the teacher will be to try something new.

It's The Law

Keep in mind: If your child attends a publicly funded institution and her behaviors interfere with her learning or the learning of others, whether or not she has a formal diagnosis, she is entitled to reasonable accommodations. We feel that 30 seconds a day or less of checking off a list is a very reasonable accommodation and one that will produce great changes in a matter of weeks. If the school refuses, go to the district office with your request. They will help you get your child's needs met in the classroom.

Quick Tip: Meeting with the teacher

1. Keep it brief

2. Keep it positive

3. Describe your success at home

4. Present the checklist

5. Welcome feedback

Basics of The Nurtured Heart Approach: What You Might Tell The Teacher

We have been using this approach at home and have had great success. We are hoping you will consider supporting us in making school a part of our child's success plan. We believe that if this approach is extended to the school day, it will make everyone's day go smoother. We thought it would help to provide you with basic information about the approach.

What is The Nurtured Heart Approach?

It was developed by a therapist to intervene with children who are intense and difficult. The approach is based on an understanding that children learn very early in life that they get more energized relationship from adults through breaking rules and pushing boundaries than they do from being "good," first described in the book *Transforming the Difficult Child: The Nurtured Heart Approach* by Howard Glasser and Jennifer Easley. Actively creating first-hand experiences of success is a way to change the child's belief that he/she gets more out of life by being adversarial.

What is the goal of the approach?

The goal is to guide the child in developing increased coping, mood regulation, initiative, and responsibility through on-going experiences of success.

Is it complicated to learn?

No. In fact, by consistently taking the stands of the approach and employing the four simple techniques, we noticed almost immediate results at home.

I am not a therapist. I am a teacher. How does this approach translate to a classroom setting?

Although it was originally designed for parents and clinicians, it has evolved into a school model that is used successfully in schools and school districts all over the country.

What if I want more information about the approach?

If you want more information, find it in *Notching Up the Nurtured Heart Approach: The New Inner Wealth Initiative for Educators,* which can be purchased along with other books on the Nurtured Heart Approach at Amazon.com or at www.childrenssuccessfoundation.com. The web site is also a useful source of information and learning opportunities as well as offering a FREE e-Course!

Step 3: Explain the System to the Child

As you did when you explained the home credit system to your child, explain that you want her to have more opportunities to earn credits and bonuses. Tell her that she now will be able to earn credits for good behavior at school. Show her the daily teacher rating note and explain it. Have her come up with some additional ways to earn credits at school, and add her ideas to the list. Explain that the credits she earns at school will be the same as those earned at home for similar behaviors. Remember, the more involved she is in creating the list, the more invested she will be in creating her own successes!

Step 4: Refueling and Accountability

At the end of the school day when the child returns home, conduct a short "refueling" and accountability session. Remember that your child has been away from his primary energy source (you) for at least six hours and is in dire need of refueling. At this point, it is profoundly important that you do not fall into the trap of refueling through negative responses.

A challenging and intense child may return from school with a strong tendency to need and seek parental attention, recognition and acknowledgment. The child needs to reconnect with you and might attempt to do this in a negative manner, such as complaining, whining, becoming sullen and sometimes even crying. That is her attempt to extract attention, reaction and focus from you in a non-affirming way. The trick is for you to anticipate this and avoid the trap of being pulled into negative payoffs.

Therefore, when your child arrives home with the checklist, avoid asking questions. Rather, say something like "It's great to see you. Let's take a look at how the day went." At that point you can give your child a bonus for responsibly bringing the note home. Continue your strategies for recognizing and building successes.

Based on the completed checklist, focus on every opportunity to acknowledge and appreciate. Using the credits and bonuses you established at home in the second step of the credit system, make sure to give the credits earned for the day. If you are using a poster, chalkboard or other accounting system, write down the earned credits in the child's "bank." Remember to be generous and give verbal recognition for every degree of success **above** the category of "Poor" or rating of "1".

A suggested conversion of teacher ratings to home credits is Poor = 0; Fair = 10; Good = 15; Very Good = 20; Excellent = 30. This would apply accordingly if you have chosen to use a 1 to 5 rating system.

Self Evaluation Ratings

You might also include in your daily school review the opportunity for your child to self-evaluate. This works well with older elementary children in particular by opening the door for more credits to be earned, not to mention developing the skill of insightfulness. (See the example that follows.)

The rules and goals should be similar to those that the teacher has rated at school so a comparison between teacher and child ratings can be made. After the child has rated himself, you add the teacher's ratings and answer any questions the child might have.

Credits will not necessarily be given for this self-evaluation sheet, but you can develop a procedure for that if you wish. The main purpose for having the child self-evaluate, however, is that it is another way to keep him invested and help him feel wealthy. And it's a great way to further the deepening process of success and inner wealth.

A sample of what a self-rating sheet might look like:

Steven's Daily Note	Teacher Rating	Steven's Rating
Today's Date: _____		
I handed in my homework.	_____	_____
I was on task in the morning.	_____	_____
I was on task in the afternoon.	_____	_____
I followed all the classroom rules.	_____	_____
I was respectful to my teachers.	_____	_____
I was respectful to my peers.		
1 = poor; 2 = fair; 3 = good; 4 = very good; 5 = excellent		

A Caution

Do not participate in any system that takes away credits for unsuccessful or unacceptable behaviors. You will defeat your overall purpose, because taking away credits still gives energy and relationship to negativity.

5 Necessary Actions to Make the Checklist for the Elementary Child a Success

First, let the child know that you will be giving as much credit as possible for good choices and behaviors made at school and that he will be able to use those credits for home privileges.

Second, explain that expectations and basic rules are the same outside the home as at home. Explain that the consequence is the same and that time-outs will be given at home for rules broken at school.

Third, inform your child before beginning the system at school that he will be held accountable at home for rules broken at school, even if the teacher or other staff person has already given a consequence there.

Fourth, make sure your child is aware that she will have a new responsibility to take the checklist to the designated person and to bring it home. Explain that she will be given a bonus for bringing the checklist home, no matter what is in the report.

Fifth, emphasize that she cannot get credit, no matter how well she did, on any day she forgets the checklist or that it hasn't been filled out by the designated person. Make it very clear when and how often the note comes home (i.e., daily, every Friday, etc.).

Eventually they begin to own it…REALLY

Co-author Lisa Bravo shared the following experience:

We decided to extend our son Christopher's credit system to the school setting but were not sure how it would work. We had so much success at home and wanted to take it a step further by giving him credits for his efforts at school. His teachers were supportive from the get go. Once Christopher got into the habit of remembering to get his note signed and he experienced even more praise, relationship, and connection over his school successes, he became vigilant about

Eventually they begin to own it – Continued

remembering his note. It became a source of pride. I can remember countless times when he would meet me at the curb, beaming, his note in hand. Other times he would see me pull up and get a panicked look on his face while telling me he had to go back in because he forgot something VERY important. He was motivated by the fact that the "store" (i.e., his earned privileges) would be closed until the next day if he forgot to bring his note home. It didn't take long before there was no need to remind or nag him – this was his obligation and he owned it!

What to do when a Child gets a "Poor" Rating

Be sure your child knows in advance that, for every "poor" rating on the checklist, she will owe you a time-out that must be completed before any after-school privileges can be redeemed. The rules of time-out will be those already established in your home.

Remember, the time-out is given in a neutral manner, and you must recognize and praise the successful, credit-earning behavior as well. One way to do this is to say: ***"Okay, let's get paid up on the time-out you owe, and we can get that out of the way."*** Remember also to keep the time-outs short AND avoid getting pulled into the trap of energizing negativity by "sermonizing."

If a major problem merits a consequence like community service, stick to your plan and administer the consequence with a continued neutral attitude. Energize the positive behaviors and any rating above "poor" by using the creative recognition techniques that have worked successfully for you at home. Always acknowledge and appreciate those ratings.

The Fantasy of the Sermon

Society believes that by discussing why something happened, especially when the child is not being successful, the child will understand and awaken to the "truth." But in reality, the awakening happens when the child IS BEING SUCCESSFUL – that is what we hold up as the TRUTH.

The Methodology for Middle School/ High School Children

Step 1: Create Your Checklist

Since older children and adolescents typically have several teachers during the day, the checklist will look a little different (see the following example) although the concept is the same. The rules/behaviors are on the left and each teacher is identified by name or initials across the top. At the bottom, you will describe the scale you have chosen to use (Poor, Fair, Good, Very Good, Excellent, or a 1 to 5 system). Each teacher then rates the child for each of the rules/goals listed. There is also space for comments the teachers might like to add.

Be sure that you have decided upon the credit values you will assign for each rating level based on your home credit system. These credits (or alternatively, consequences) are awarded at the time you review the child's completed checklist for the day, week or whatever you have previously decided.

Here is an example of the checklist described above:

	JM	LB	DH	MB	NG	RW	RZ
Teacher's Initials	—	—	—	—	—	—	—
Homework Handed In	—	—	—	—	—	—	—
Appropriate Behavior	—	—	—	—	—	—	—
Participated	—	—	—	—	—	—	—

Scale 1-5: 1 = poor; 2 = fair; 3 = good; 4 = very good; 5 = excellent

Comments

_____

Here is another example of what a checklist for a child with more than one teacher might look like:

Student: _____ Date: _____

1st Hour: Mr. Brock

Homework Handed In	1	2	3	4	5
Behavior Appropriate	1	2	3	4	5
Participated	1	2	3	4	5

Teacher's Signature: _____ Comments: _____

_____

2nd Hour: Ms. Hufford

Homework Handed In	1	2	3	4	5
Behavior Appropriate	1	2	3	4	5
Participated	1	2	3	4	5

Teacher's Signature: _____ Comments: _____

_____

3rd Hour: Mrs. Cooper

Homework Handed In	1	2	3	4	5
Behavior Appropriate	1	2	3	4	5
Participated	1	2	3	4	5

Teacher's Signature: _____ Comments: _____

_____

Scale 1-5: 1 = poor; 2 = fair; 3 = good; 4 = very good; 5 = excellent

Note: We recommend that the child bring the checklist to school daily and return it daily until she is in the habit of getting it completed. Once the child has demonstrated consistent positive behaviors and success at school, consider allowing more time between notes home.

Step 2: Meet with the Teachers

If at all possible, arrange to meet with your child's teachers, using the same approach as described earlier in this section. You might schedule this through the school counselor, special education coordinator, or principal as needed. If it is not possible to meet with all of your child's teachers, often the homeroom teacher or school counselor is a good compromise. Explain your goals, the basics of The Nurtured Heart Approach, your successes at home, and your desire to keep this as simple as possible for the school staff.

Remember to be fully prepared in advance and, for each teacher, bring a sample of the checklist and an explanation letter. Be sure to ask for the teachers' input within the parameters of your home credit system, and let them know that you will be giving your child a consequence for any "poor" ratings regardless of consequences administered by any of the teachers.

Don't forget to stress the idea of partial credits so that your child can feel some sense of success. And finally, be sure to emphasize that your child will be totally responsible for taking the ratings checklists to each teacher and retrieving them after each class, as well as for bringing them home at the end of the day. If meetings are not possible, use the letter approach described earlier, and follow-up with phone calls.

Step 3: Explain the System to Your Child

Explain to your child that you want him to have more opportunity to earn credits and bonuses for good behaviors. Show him the teacher checklist and explain how it works. Make it clear that he will be responsible for seeing that each teacher rates and signs the checklist and for bringing it home from school. As stated earlier, we recommend a daily system until the child has demonstrated consistency in choosing appropriate behavior and achieving success at school. Explain that the credits he earns at school will concur with those already established at home for similar behaviors. **REMEMBER**: the more involved he is in creating his list, the more invested he will be in creating his own successes!

Step 4: Refueling and Accountability

Every child, no matter their age, will still require "refueling" at the end of the day. Remember not to fall into the trap of refueling through negative responses. Merely say something like: *"It's great to see you. Let's take a look at how the day went."*

During this refueling and school review period, be sure to acknowledge and appreciate at every opportunity. Give verbal recognition for every degree of success **above** the "Poor" category or **above** a "1" rating. Be sure to take the opportunity to award bonus points whenever appropriate, and especially for the extra responsibility your child has exhibited in seeing that the checklist was taken to school, filled out by each teacher and brought home. You can use the same conversion of teacher ratings to home credits as for the elementary child above, or you can total the ratings from each teacher on a given behavior and devise your own credit values.

5 Necessary Actions to Make the Checklist for the Older Child/ Adolescent a Success

First, inform your child that because things are going so much better at home, you want to help her convert her efforts at school into credits that can be spent at home. Let her know that you've come up with a way to help her teachers report her positive actions and efforts by using a note that will be converted to points and will allow you to applaud her each day after school.

Second, let your child know you will be giving as much credit as possible for ratings **above** "Poor" (or **above** "1") and that she will be able to use those credits for home privileges. As usual, however, privileges cannot be earned until after any time-out (and community service when applicable) is served.

Third, make sure your older child or adolescent knows that she is solely responsible for taking the ratings checklist to school every day (or according to your frequency schedule), seeing that each teacher rates and signs it, and bringing it home on schedule. Any breach of this responsibility will result in a consequence, while being responsible will earn the child bonus points.

Fourth, any rating of "Poor" (or "1") will result in a time-out. Remember to keep time-outs short and use the time-out rules you have already established in your home. Older children and adolescents are more likely to need community service occasionally than will the younger child. In all cases, whether it is time-out alone or time-out with community service, avoid being drawn into negativity by inquisition or discussion of the problem or issue.

Fifth, always continue to energize the positive behaviors. Remember that any rating **above** "Poor" (or **above**"1") is a success. Use the creative recognition techniques that have worked so successfully for you at home. Always acknowledge and appreciate any effort toward success.

Community Service for Older Children/ Adolescents

Community service can be assigned for major infractions. (If you have established a credit system, you have already determined what constitutes a major infraction and have explained this to your older child/adolescent.) We define "community" as any setting outside your teenager's room, which therefore would include your home or neighborhood. Community service involves activities in addition to chores, but they should be things that can reasonably be accomplished despite being a "consequence." For example, you may not want to assign community service that requires you to drive your child to another location. The goal is for her to be able to complete the service with as little direction from you as possible.

Remember to deliver the community service directive in an unceremonious manner. Say something like, *"For your community service, you will need to clean the garage. The 'store' will be open when you are finished, but not until then."* Or *"As soon as you get your community service done, let me know. I am looking forward to adding up all the credits you've earned today."* Refrain from lecturing and give abundant, energized praise when work has been completed. It is advisable to place parameters on the time-frame – so the community service might be anywhere from 10 minutes to 10 hours of the particular task or chore, depending on the severity of the transgression.

Some Ideas for Community Service:

Cleaning the garage

Washing the family car

Picking up litter in the neighborhood

Picking weeds

Washing windows

Cleaning the yard for an elderly neighbor

Bathing the dog

Dusting/Vacuuming

Cleaning the litter box

Folding/Putting away the laundry

The School Link-Up: Frequently Asked Questions

Why is it a good idea to extend my child's credit system to the school setting?

Perhaps the best reason to link home and school (as well as other outside settings as needed) is the powerful support factor that results from crediting as many successful behaviors as possible. Without such a system, children typically under-emphasize how the day went, and they communicate only few bits of specific information. A basic, simple feedback system between school and home provides you with specific knowledge about the child's day, which allows you many more opportunities to verbalize appreciation and use positive efforts as incentives. This is also a way for overly needy children to refuel after many hours of separation from their parent(s).

If a child is not re-energized positively, the likelihood of negative acting out – as an alternative route to achieve connection – will increase. And, as you now know, that is a less nutritious way of reconnecting. The proactive aspect of intervention alone makes a huge difference in how the remainder of the day goes.

In addition, when children are aware that feedback from school goes home to parents (the idea that God/the parent is watching), they generally are more motivated to behave well. The feedback system may also serve to encourage other care providers to more frequently offer up their own recognition and appreciation of positive behaviors. Feedback keeps you better informed about how well the out-of-home support and structure are meeting your child's needs. Also, this process often can be directly integrated into the school's Individualized Education Plan (IEP) for your child to further increase school support.

What if my intense child resists this school credit system or it just doesn't seem to be working?

Keep in mind that very intense children are going to test the system, just as they probably did when you first implemented it in your home. To make sense of this new element in their lives, the difficult child has to challenge the system to see if it will hold up under fire. She needs to know that the system will support her success with a lot more energy than it did her failures. At the start, it is likely the difficult child will manifest this challenge by actually promoting poor ratings from the teachers (via poor behaviors) or by intentionally trying to sabotage the system. It is important to anticipate this, and if it happens take a stand and ride it out. Your child will settle into this change once she sees that you have the best of intentions and that you are not going to fall apart if she resists. Here are some crucial points to keep in mind.

First, the child will need to trust that YOU will notice, credit and show excitement over all the degrees of positive choices reported, day in and day out.

Second, he will need to see that every challenge will result in accountability, no matter what, and that you will respond with the same neutral attitude.

Third, he must see that the emotional payoffs – the verbal and nonverbal energy and relationship that you radiate – only exist for the positive behaviors and NOT for negative behaviors. Progress can take hold and take off once a child determines that his parents are really going to hold him accountable for his school behaviors. In effect you now have established overriding authority wrapped in a balanced and healthy way of being powerfully influential. The exciting part is that you will see this positive influence regardless of whether or not the school staff improves their ways of working with intense children.

It has been our experience that even with the most challenging children, if you stick with the program, you will begin to see a turnaround at school within the first month.

Secondary Benefits for Intense Children

You will notice a number of secondary payoffs of extending the credit system to the school. Once the child is able to shift into more "typical" levels of classroom behavior, the outcome will no doubt be a better relationship between teacher and child. Any adversity between teacher and child that might have existed will decrease because the teacher is seeing that his efforts are helping to improve the child's classroom behavior. Even a teacher who might not have been too excited about the system initially will notice the changes occurring in his student. Once the relationship has shifted to success, we have found the teacher to be quite willing to share in the celebration of the child's successes.

Another powerful secondary benefit is social success achieved with peers as the child becomes more likeable and ultimately more accepted by the peer group. Remember, the more success the child experiences in the school environment, the more invested he will become as both a student and a friend.

The Wrap Up

- Extending the credit system to the school provides powerful support for what you are doing at home by helping the child improve his behavior in settings outside the home.

- This method is normally only recommended if there is an existing school issue, but occasionally parents will make use of this to simply build on the school success they already have.

- Teachers, although very well-meaning, might not have the tools for managing and disciplining a very difficult child, but you have had great success using The Nurtured Heart Approach with your child.

- You have a new understanding of your "ever-present" relationship with your child and how that relationship can be used through this reporting system to impart the perception that you are watching as well as motivating your child.

- The basic steps involved in extending the system to school are: preparing the checklists, informing school personnel of the system, soliciting their cooperation, explaining the system to the child and providing daily refueling and accountability.

- With some children, initial efforts might produce a bumpy start and they might challenge the system, but if you stick with it by showing excitement over positive choices and you are consistent in providing neutral time-outs, you will see the turnaround you are seeking.

- There are secondary payoffs by way of improved classroom relationships, both with the teacher and with peers.

CONGRATULATIONS! You have come to the end of the four phases of The Nurtured Heart Approach – an interesting, exciting and rewarding journey. Please stay with us as we take a few extra moments of your time to talk about things we have learned about the approach that we think will prove encouraging and helpful to you.

CHAPTER 6

Our Take Home Message

As therapists who specialize in working with children with problems beyond the ordinary, it is not unusual that we receive referrals to help a child who has previously been diagnosed with disorders such as bipolar disorder, oppositional defiant disorder, and attention-deficit/hyperactivity disorder, to name a few.

When we see these diagnoses applied to children, and especially children as young as three years old, our hearts ache. We understand that for treatment and payment (i.e., insurance) purposes, diagnosis is helpful. Diagnostic labels can be dangerous, however. They lead us to see the diagnosed child in a negative light and to expect negative behavior. Diagnoses also encourage us to attribute negative behaviors to the disorder – to see the child's behavior as predetermined.

Deterministic thinking seems to us to be circular. It is not productive, and neither is it creative. Further, it implies there is little hope for the future.

Recently other psychologists and professionals have warned us against the dangers of this kind of narrow thinking. It is a one-dimensional way of looking at the problem that infers it is all inside the child. When a parent brings a child to a doctor seeking a solution, it inherently implies that we are trying to fix the child rather than understanding the powerful influences of outside factors. For example, scholars have pointed out that factors external to the individual, such as family, school, and other cultural influences, also "shape and mold the course of the individual's life" (Hinshaw, S.P. [2004]. *Lessons learned, messages received, ideas transmitted.* Attention, August, 2004, p. 34).

Dr. Hinshaw also noted that "The brain is highly plastic: genes may require the effects of environmental influences to be expressed, and destiny does not reside wholly in genetic determinism…." In other words, we all come here with a genetic makeup but our environment determines how it is played out. A real life example of the plasticity of the brain and "hope for the future" is provided in the story of the famed life of Dr. Ben Carson, Director of Pediatric Neurosurgery at Johns Hopkins Children's Center. In an article he wrote for Parade Magazine (Carson, G. *Your Mind Can Map Your Destiny.* Parade. NY Dec. 7, 2003), Dr. Carson explained that he grew up in poverty in Detroit and Boston. He started out with "terrible grades, anger and low self-esteem." "But," he wrote, "once I made a decision to change my life by harnessing the power of my mind, nothing could stand in my way."

Dr. Carson credited his transformation to the firm guidance of his mother and his own determination. His academic improvement was "so dramatic that one might have suspected a brain transplant, if such a thing were possible," he wrote. Dr. Carson forcefully added, ***"The actual change occurred in my self-perception and my expectations. I had gone from victim to master planner."***

This powerful example helps us understand the difference between the negative thinking that can arise from a deterministic approach and the bright future that arises when one transforms his thinking to the positive possibilities. With the help of his mother, Dr. Carson "transformed" himself. He clearly learned to **see himself in a new, positive light of GREATNESS.**

This is what we hope The Nurtured Heart Approach has conveyed to you. Can you see how vitally important it is that you see your child **in a new, positive light of GREATNESS?** Our children DO NOT have to live the legacy of their propensities. Their futures are NOT determined by a diagnosis. There IS hope for the future. All we have to do is change our perspective, understand that they (and we in turn) can be transformed, and finally possess in ourselves the determination, firm commitment and THE APPROACH to guide our children toward their own transformation. They will do the rest themselves.

The Nurtured Heart Approach is really about *GREATNESS*. What does greatness look like? At some point in this journey, it became so apparent that this was an entirely different kind of software – a new kind of download that once in the internal drive, keeps upgrading itself automatically in the most pleasantly surprising ways. This seems to lead to trusting your children from the inside out – they now hold their own keys to the kingdom and have their very own wisdom that applies so perfectly to their life. You are simply watering your child's seeds of GREATNESS. When adequately nourished, he will have a delightful and wonderful life of his own.

This is a book whose purpose is to make YOU, the parent, feel great by allowing you to clearly see and feel – in body, heart and soul – that you are having not just a GOOD impact but rather a GREAT impact on your child's core being and the GREATNESS he or she manifests. It is a book with a further purpose of giving your child the thrilling experience of flourishing, not the ordinary road of childhood, but rather an extraordinary highway of living a life of GREATNESS. This kind of wealth – inner wealth – is perhaps the best inheritance of all. With the tools of this approach fully embraced, we now have the ability to create for ourselves and our children what our world will look like. We create our own happiness, our own opportunities, our own successes. We create each day, each moment, each interaction. No longer do we have to buy into the belief that we are at the mercy of our propensities and that we must wait for the world to change in order to experience true joy. Each moment is now an opportunity to live "IN JOY" at all times.

The following is an example of how one parent went about inspiring her child's GREATNESS.

Bringing Home The Greatness

Beth, a very intense, but very bright and friendly 17-year old, was often very disagreeable and easy to anger. Like most children, she had her share of moments, and in those moments, mostly ones concerning hotly contested limits, she could fire off words and actions that could rock the walls at home and make life very uncomfortable for days on end.

Once her mother learned The Nurtured Heart Approach, she chose to purposely "create" successes at times when the arguments weren't happening. These times became windows of opportunity to deliver not only messages of *gratefulness*, but she also chose to identify Beth's actions as aspects of her greatness.

Here is an example: *"Beth, you looked for a second like you thought about lashing out when I said no to a snack, but you didn't. You are choosing not to argue and I am very grateful. You are being thoughtful and considerate, and those are great qualities that I admire a lot."*

Can a 17-year-old hear statements like this? Absolutely! She has heard them a lot better than the long-winded attempts to reason or argue with her in the past when she went off on a tirade.

Beth hasn't argued in years and now has tremendous inner strength and ability to use that same passion in intensely wonderful ways.

Here are other related appreciative comments that Beth's mom adamantly chose to make on a regular basis – wonderful examples of the stand that you, as well, can take on greatness:

- I so appreciate your great sense of right and wrong in deciding to study for the test over being at the mall – even though your friends tried to pressure you.

- I want to acknowledge you for not using swear words when you were mad earlier. The great thing was that you expressed your anger without breaking any rules. You really showed us wonderful judgment in just explaining what it was that was upsetting, and when you do that you show respect for yourself and us. Respect and good judgment are qualities of greatness in you that I see and admire.

- You have been so helpful around the house today and in such a tuned-in way to my needs and my stress about getting the house ready for the holidays. I really love that about you. Being tuned in to others is such a great quality.

- You continue to show such kindness to our pets and it warms my heart. It just makes me so appreciative of your spirit and how special you are in treating all living things so well. It really makes me trust you so much. You have so many qualities of greatness and your kindness is one that really warms my heart.

Remember, "gratefulness" and "greatness" go hand in hand when we are honestly reflecting their truly positive qualities back to our children.

BRAVO! BRAVO! BRAVO! BRAVO! BRAVO!

You have come to the end of this workbook! Thank you so much for allowing us the honor of assisting you through this process. You have taken risks, learned new notions, new skills, and new ways of looking at things. You have fostered renewed relationships.

If you have not yet witnessed a full-blown transformation, we hope you have, at the very least, glimpsed the promised land of an awakening. You have become resolute about how to energize positivity and greatness, about how not to energize negativity, and about how to create limits and a truer version of accountability.

CONGRATULATIONS!!! These are huge steps. You have kept an open mind and heart, allowing the healing power of your heart and this approach to take hold. We tip our hats to you for your brilliance and your greatness! As you drink in the truth of your own greatness, know that you are creating a new and richer relationship with your amazing child by way of the great positive influence you keep choosing to exercise. BRAVO!!!! Thank you for making the world a kinder, warmer, gentler, brighter, more loving place!

ACKNOWLEDGEMENTS

It is absolutely amazing to me that this volume has finally made its way into form. So many people have come along over the years and suggested a workbook and each and every time I would say "go for it" and each and every time the project, though well intended, would fall apart for one reason or another. That is until this time. And the timing couldn't have been better. Had a workbook emerged years ago it would not have captured all the new ways The Nurtured Heart Approach has come to life and evolved and improved.

Thank God for Joann Bowdidge and Lisa Bravo. They are so brilliantly skilled in this approach. Without them this book would have never happened. They were the perfect inspiring collaborators for this project. They are so greatly talented as clinicians and so greatly motivating and thrilling as co-authors. Through all the precious effort and heart put into this volume they have made it so attuned to the needs of the reader.

For making these and numerous other pieces of the puzzle come together, I am indebted to Joann and Lisa.

Sadly, Joann passed away after a battle with cancer shortly after this book was first published in 2008. We dedicate this revised edition in 2013 to the beauty of Joann's brilliance and spirit, which continues to support and uplift us.

I am indebted to Michael Kichler, not only for his amazing talent as a graphic artist but for his amazing attitude in making this book come to life. Thank you for your great contribution.

I greatly appreciate the brilliant editing and polishing that Chris Howell brought to the first edition of this book and I am greatly appreciative of Melissa Block who worked so brilliant to diligently bring all the updates to this revised 2013 version.

Thank you to all who have taken an interest in The Nurtured Heart Approach and who have inspired my dedication to the greatness of our children and the greatness of all.

And lastly, thank you to all the angels who keep dancing in support and celebration of this approach's impact in homes, schools and treatment programs around the world and to evolving this approach as a vehicle to that end.

Howard Glasser

Little did I know when I walked out of a workshop presented by Howard Glasser in Kansas City in the spring of 2003 that I would eventually be engaged in a project helping to write a workbook for parents on The Nurtured Heart Approach. All I knew at that time was that I had spent an entire day hearing about a marvelous new approach to working with children that was a stirring breath of fresh air. I wanted to know more. And so I satisfied that desire by attending the full-week training for certification in Tucson in the winter of 2004.

That pursuit of knowledge about this fascinating and effective approach eventually led to a tremendous desire to tell others and help them learn about The Nurtured Heart Approach. To that end, I sent my early efforts to Howard for his approval, and he immediately shot back to me that we had the embryonic makings of a parent workbook, and he asked me if I would be interested in helping with such a project. My answer was not "no."

So, Howie, Lisa and I met in the late spring of 2005 and began drafting our ideas about this workbook. Ideas came and went, and pages were written, critiqued and rewritten but all of our efforts over the many months have culminated in what you now hold in your hands.

The trek to completion of this book was absolutely fascinating. As a team, on a regular basis we were able to share our clinical experiences using The Nurtured Heart Approach, and we found sustenance and energy in that participation. From being almost perfect strangers when we began, we grew to appreciate the strengths and creativity of each other and to love one another dearly. Tremendous thanks go to Howard Glasser for creating this approach, sharing it with me and constantly encouraging me, helping me along my spiritual path, and spurring me on to reach further into myself to bring out my best; to Jennifer Easley, whom I have yet to meet, for helping Howie put together his first book in such a clear manner; and to Lisa Bravo for her marvelous insights and creativity, as well as for her sweet spirit and willingness to share the successes she has had with her own children using The Nurtured Heart Approach.

Thanks also go to Dale and Dottie Halfaker, who own our practice and have allowed me time, facilities and resources to work on this book. Thanks to Curt Mattson, our practicum student, for his technical support. Thanks to Robin Hood, our office manager, who always got the team's many conference calls through to me with dispatch. Great thanks to my wonderful husband, John, for his constant encouragement and to my daughter Holly Bowdidge Stone for her feedback about The Nurtured Heart Approach, which she has used with such success with her son (my grandson), Ben. Finally, thanks to all of those people in my life who have encouraged, mentored and believed in me. They have contributed much to who I am today. They are too numerous to mention, but I remember their remarkable contributions to my life and thank each of them for that.

Joann Ridenour Bowdidge

My career as a difficult child has brought me to this pinnacle. Every tear that has been shed and every painful experience has guided me to this place. I embrace all of it, without question. I am forever grateful for all of my wise teachers and guides who entered my life at just the right moment. I tip my hat to all of my dear friends and family – thank you for loving me through the rollercoaster ride!

To my parents who did their best with the tools they had. Dad, you taught me how to work hard and be passionate about what I love. To my mother who courageously healed her wounds and then graciously fought her biggest battle. You died an insightful, wise, loving and passionate woman. I know you are smiling on me today, mom.

Thank you, Dave, for loving me ALWAYS and in ALL WAYS. You held a vision and purpose for me that went far beyond what I felt capable of. Thank you for taking this journey with me and for supporting me in creating a better world. NONE of this would have happened without you.

To wonderful Christopher and magnificent Danielle – thank you for always being the brightest stars in my sky, for loving me in the yummiest of ways, and for teaching me how to be wise. This book would not be nearly the same without your stories of success. Your generosity and commitment to believing "every kid deserves to be a Nurtured Heart Kid" is a testament to your greatness and love. I am in awe of you both.

To Gretchen and Lynn Hankins – thank you for showing me unconditional love and for introducing me to my greatness. To Judie Bernstein – my "adopted" mother – words fail to express the impact you have had on me as a woman, mother, and human being. To Debbie, who showed me what it is to REALLY be a good mother. To my CarriageWay family – your support and encouragement have been unwavering. Thanks for always nurturing my heart.

To my Nurtured Heart family: I have been profoundly changed by your magical and transformative love. To Joann Bowdidge – your patience and persistence is inspiring. Collaborating with you has been a pleasure and an honor! Your presence in my life and on this earth has been truly missed. This book is a legacy to your greatness! Thanks for keeping us on track. To Michael Kichler, for your friendship and your unbelievable gift for bringing this workbook to life through your talents as an artist.

Finally and most especially, I want to thank Howard Glasser, my dear friend and mentor. I am forever changed and profoundly grateful for having listened to my angels on the day I finally introduced myself to you. That was a defining moment in my life and I have never been the same since. Thank you for believing in me and encouraging me through this process. You are, undoubtedly, among the greatest men I have ever known.

I dedicate this book to the hundreds of families who took a leap of faith and allowed me to guide them down a different road. This book is dedicated to all of you moms, dads, teachers, administrators, therapists, nurses, doctors, and probation officers that took stand and made a difference in the life of a child. This workbook came to light because of my experiences with all of you. I am honored to have been a part of your journey. I dedicate this book to the children and teens that I was fortunate enough to have known. Thanks for giving the world another chance and for letting me walk with you for a while. The next chapter is yet to be written!

Lisa Bravo

ABOUT THE AUTHORS

Howard, Joann and Lisa

Howard Glasser is the founder of the Children's Success Foundation and creator of the Nurtured Heart Approach™, which has been used in hundreds of thousands of homes and classrooms around the world. Teaching adults how to nurture greatness in children is his life's work.

He is author of ***Transforming the Difficult Child*** currently the top-selling book on the topic of ADHD and otherwise challenging children; ***The Inner Wealth Initiative***, one of the leading books on school interventions; ***You Are Oprah – Igniting the Fires of Greatness***, a book that outlines ways to apply the Nurtured Heart Approach to one's self; and ***All Children Flourishing***, a book that describes the approach's use with all children, difficult or not. Four of his eight books are in the top one percent of all books on Amazon.com.

Howard has been a featured guest on CNN and a consultant for 48 Hours. He currently teaches the Nurtured Heart Approach through live presentations worldwide. He has consulted for numerous psychiatric, judicial and educational programs.

Although he has done extensive doctoral work in the fields of Clinical Psychology and Educational Leadership, he feels his own years as a difficult child contributed the most to his understanding of the needs of challenging children and to the success of his approach, which is based on aligning the energies of relationship. His work also supports many children in developing the inner strength to resist addictive substances.

Howard has been considered one of the world's most influential voices in the movement to prevent unnecessary psychiatric medicating of children.

Joann Ridenour Bowdidge, M.A. in clinical psychology, is a licensed psychologist in Missouri, practicing currently at Neuropsychological Associates of Southwest Missouri. She has extensive experience performing psychological evaluations and working with difficult children, including those with behavior disorders, AD/HD, and learning disabilities. In addition, Joann has worked in a community mental health center; in a rehabilitation hospital for those with head injury, spinal cord injury, stroke and other neurological illnesses; in public schools, undergraduate and graduate educational settings as a teacher and consultant; in Head Start as a program planner and clinician; and as a private practitioner. Currently, Joann also travels to communities in Missouri to lecture, teach and excite others about The Nurtured Heart Approach. Her extensive experience with many types of disorders of adults and children has contributed to her insights in regard to the needs of difficult children and their parents. She lives in Springfield, Missouri.

Lisa Bravo, M.C., is the Clinical Director for The Children's Success Foundation (www.childrenssuccessfoundation.com) and Master Co-facilitator for the Nurtured Heart Certification Programs, along with Howard Glasser. She is author of the ***Notching Up! The Nurtured Heart Approach Workbook For Educators*** (2011) Lisa brings 25 years combined experience in the area of parenting, counseling, chemical dependency, and crisis intervention. She is the founder and director of Parentworx Counseling & Consulting (www.parentworx.com), providing services for parents, schools, and agencies both locally and nationally. To date, she has trained a multitude of parents, teachers, schools, executives, administrators, and mental health providers how to implement the approach. Lisa joyfully resides in Gilbert, Arizona, with her husband and two teenagers.